Reteach
Chapter 1

Name _____

What you should learn:

1.1	How to use numbers to identify and measure objects and how to recognize and describe number patterns

---

Examples   *Identifying and Measuring and Describing Number Patterns*

a. Numbers can be used to represent how fast an object is moving. If an automobile is traveling at a speed of 45 miles per hour, is the speed of the automobile less than or more than the speed limit of 55 miles per hour?

The speed of the auto traveling at 45 miles per hour is less than the speed limit of 55 miles per hour.

b. Describe a pattern for this sequence. Use the pattern to list the next three numbers in the sequence.

$$3, 6, 9, 12, \boxed{?}, \boxed{?}, \boxed{?}$$

One pattern for this sequence is that each number is 3 more than the preceding number. The next three numbers are 15, 18, 21.

c. Describe a pattern for this sequence. Use the pattern to list the next three numbers in the sequence.

$$81, 27, 9, 3, \boxed{?}, \boxed{?}, \boxed{?}$$

One pattern for this sequence is that each number is one-third of the preceding number. The next three numbers are $1, \frac{1}{3}, \frac{1}{9}$.

Guidelines:

- You can use numbers to identify and measure real-life objects.
- An ordered list of numbers is called a sequence.
- You can describe a pattern for a sequence and use the pattern to write the next numbers in the sequence.

EXERCISES

In Exercises 1–3, write the first 6 numbers in the sequence.

1. The first number is 14. Each succeeding number is 5 more than the preceding number.

2. The first number is $\frac{1}{2}$. Each succeeding number is twice as large as the preceding number.

3. The first number is 18. Each succeeding number is 3 less than the preceding number.

In Exercises 4–6, describe the pattern. Then list the next 3 numbers.

4. $7, 11, 15, 19, \boxed{?}, \boxed{?}, \boxed{?}$

5. $10, 100, 1000, 10{,}000, \boxed{?}, \boxed{?}, \boxed{?}$

6. $33, 28, 23, 18, \boxed{?}, \boxed{?}, \boxed{?}$

Reteach
Chapter 1

Name _____

What you should learn:

| **1.2** | How to use the four basic number operations and how to use multiplication models. |

Correlation to Pupil's Textbook:

Chapter Test (p. 47)

Exercises 8–11

Examples   *Using Number Operations and Using Multiplication Models*

a. Write a verbal description of the number sentence.

$\frac{18}{6} = 3$ The quotient of 18 and 6 is 3.

b. Find the sum or difference.

The difference of 0.4 and 0.1 is 0.3.   Verbal description

$0.4 - 0.1 = 0.3$ Symbolic description

c. Find the product or quotient.

The quotient of 207 and 23 is 9.   Verbal description

$207 \div 23 = 9$ Symbolic description

d. Show how to use area to model the product of 2 and 5. Use squares to form a rectangle that is 2 units wide and 5 units long. Count the squares, each of which has an area of 1 square unit. The rectangle has an area of 10 square units.

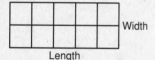 Width / Length

(Area of rectangle) $=$ (Width) $\times$ (Length)

10 square units $= 2 \times 5$

Guidelines:

- The four basic number operations are addition, subtraction, multiplication, and division.
- You can write a verbal description of a number sentence.
- You can use a model to help you visualize or understand a process or object.
- You can use area as a model for multiplication.

EXERCISES

In Exercises 1–8, find the sum, difference, product, or quotient.

1. $313.4 + 25.7$ **2.** $425 - 398$ **3.** 51×18 **4.** $\dfrac{4329}{13}$

5. $(7.3)(12.5)$ **6.** $18 + 29 + 62$ **7.** $0.345 - 0.063$ **8.** $223.2 \div 0.8$

In Exercises 9 and 10, write a number sentence.

9. ⊞ + ▯ = ⊞

10. ⊞ = ⊞ − ▯

Reteach
Chapter 1

Name _____

What you should learn:

1.3	How to use powers and how to use square roots.

Correlation to Pupil's Textbook:

Mid-Chapter Self-Test (p. 22)   **Chapter Test (p. 47)**

Exercises 12, 13   Exercise 16

Examples | *Using Powers and Using Square Roots*

a. Write a verbal description of the number sentence.

$6^3 = 216$ 6 raised to the 3rd power or 6 cubed is 216.

b. Write each expression as a power. Then use a calculator to find the value of the power.

$4 \times 4 \times 4$ 4^3 Calculator steps: $4 \boxed{y^x} 3 \boxed{=} 64$

$(0.5)(0.5)(0.5)(0.5)$ $(0.5)^4$ Calculator steps: $0.5 \boxed{y^x} 4 \boxed{=} 0.0625$

c. Find the value of the expression using a calculator. Round your result to two decimal places.

$\sqrt{6.27}$ Calculator steps: $6.27 \boxed{\sqrt{}} \approx 2.50$

d. Find the number that is represented by $\triangle$.

$\sqrt{\triangle} = 11$ $\triangle = 121$

e. Find the side of a square which has an area of 44.89 square units.

$(\text{Side})^2 = 44.89$

$\text{Side} = \sqrt{44.89} = 6.7$ units

Guidelines:

- A power has two parts, a base and an exponent.
- Any number can be used as an exponent.
- When you square the square root of a number n, you get the original number n. $\left(\sqrt{n}\right)^2 = n$
- The square root of a perfect square can be written as an exact decimal.

EXERCISES

In Exercises 1–3, write a verbal description of each number sentence.

1. $\sqrt{0.09} = 0.3$ **2.** $2^5 = 32$ **3.** $\sqrt{484} = 22$

In Exercises 4–6, write each expression as a power. Then use a calculator when appropriate to find the value of the power.

4. $\frac{1}{3} \cdot \frac{1}{3}$ **5.** $(6.7)(6.7)(6.7)(6.7)$ **6.** $(15)(15)(15)$

In Exercises 7–9, find the value of the expression using a calculator. Round your result to two decimal places.

7. $\sqrt{201}$ **8.** $\sqrt{4.6}$ **9.** $\sqrt{1.44}$

Reteach
Chapter 1

What you should learn:

| 1.4 | How to use order of operations and how to use order of operations on a calculator. |

Correlation to Pupil's Textbook:

Mid-Chapter Self-Test (p. 22) **Chapter Test (p. 47)**
Exercises 14–18   Exercises 9–12

Examples *Using the Order of Operations and Evaluating Expressions with a Calculator*

a. Use the Priority of Operations to evaluate the expression.

$$16 \div 2^3 = 16 \div 8 \qquad \textit{First priority: exponent}$$
$$= 2 \qquad \textit{Second priority: division}$$

b. Use the Left-to-Right Rule to evaluate the expression.

$$24 \div 4 \times 2 = 6 \times 2 \qquad \textit{Left-to-Right Rule: divide}$$
$$= 12 \qquad \textit{Multiply.}$$

c. Use a calculator to evaluate the expression.

$$2 + 4^3 - 36$$

If your calculator uses the Order of Operations used in the textbook, it should display 30.

Guidelines:

- A numerical expression is collection of numbers, operations, and grouping symbols.
- You are evaluating an expression when you perform the operations to obtain a single number.
- The Order of Operations is used to evaluate an expression involving more than one operation, using the order:
  1. First do operations that occur within grouping symbols.
  2. Then evaluate powers.
  3. Then do multiplications and divisions from left to right.
  4. Finally do additions and subtractions from left to right.

EXERCISES

In Exercises 1–6, evaluate the expression without using a calculator. Use a calculator to check your answer.

1. $18 - 5 + 3$

2. $5 + 6 \div 3 \times 7$

3. $4 \times 20 - 6^2$

4. $12 \div (18 - 15) \cdot 2$

5. $(9 + 13) \cdot 3 - 8$

6. $5^2 + (9 - 5) \div 4$

What you should learn:

| 1.5 | How to evaluate variable expressions and how to use variable expressions to model real-life situations |

Correlation to Pupil's Textbook:

Chapter Test (p. 47)
Exercises 1–6

Examples *Evaluating Variable Expressions and Modeling Real-life Situations*

a. Evaluate the algebraic expression $4x^2 + 5x$ for $x = 3$.

$4x^2 + 5x$	*Write the expression.*
$4x^2 + 5x = 4(3)^2 + 5(3)$	*Substitute 3 for x.*
$= 4(9) + 15$	*Simplify $(3)^2$ and $5(3)$.*
$= 36 + 15$	*Simplify $4(9)$.*
$= 51$	*Value of the expression*

b. A truck is traveling at a speed of 80 kilometers per hour. How far does the truck travel in 2.5 hours?

Verbal model $\boxed{\text{Distance}} = \boxed{\text{Rate}} \cdot \boxed{\text{Time}}$

Distance $= d$ (kilometers)
Speed $= r$ (kilometers per hour)
Time $= t$ (hours)

$d = rt$	*Write algebraic model.*
$= (80)(2.5)$	*Substitute for r and t.*
$= 200$	*Simplify.*

In 2.5 hours, the truck travels 200 kilometers.

Guidelines:

- A variable is a letter that is used to represent one or more numbers.
- An algebraic expression is a collection of numbers, variables, operations, and grouping symbols.
- To evaluate an algebraic expression, use the following flow chart.

| Write the algebraic expression | → | Substitute values for variables | → | Simplify the numerical expression |

- A formula (or algebraic model) can be written as a verbal model.

EXERCISES

In Exercises 1–8, evaluate the expression for $a = 3$, and $b = 2$.

1. $(a + b)4$

2. ba

3. $5b - 2a$

4. $(2b + a)^2$

5. $(a + b) \div (a - b)$

6. $4b^3 a$

7. $a^4 - 5b$

8. $3b^2 \cdot 2a$

9. How far does the truck in Example b travel in 4.5 hours?

What you should learn:

1.6	How to use tables to organize data and how to use graphs to model data visually

Correlation to Pupil's Textbook:

Chapter Test (p. 47)
Exercises 17–21

Examples *Using Tables to Organize Data and Using Graphs to Organize Data*

a. The federal minimum wage increased 5 times from 1978 to 1991. The wages were as follows. (Source: The Milwaukee Journal, 3/14/93)

2.65	1978	3.35	1983	3.35	1988
2.90	1979	3.35	1984	3.35	1989
3.10	1980	3.35	1985	3.80	1990
3.35	1981	3.35	1986	4.25	1991
3.35	1982	3.35	1987		

Represent this data by a table.

Year	1978	1979	1980	1981	1982	1983	1984	1985	1986	1987	1988	1989	1990	1991
Minimum Wage	2.65	2.90	3.10	3.35	3.35	3.35	3.35	3.35	3.35	3.35	3.35	3.35	3.80	4.25

b. Draw a line graph that represents the minimum wage data given in Example a above.

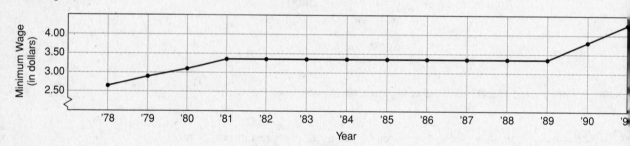

Guidelines:

- The word data is plural and it means facts or numbers that describe something.
- A collection of data is easier to understand when it is organized in a table, a bar graph, or a line graph.

EXERCISE

The minimum and average Major League baseball salary from 1981 to 1991 is given as follows. (Source: Major League Baseball Players Association)

32,500/185,651 (1981)	60,000/371,571 (1985)	68,000/497,254 (1989)
33,500/241,497 (1982)	60,000/412,520 (1986)	100,000/597,537 (1990)
35,000/289,194 (1983)	62,500/412,454 (1987)	100,000/851,492 (1991)
40,000/329,408 (1984)	62,500/438,729 (1988)	

Represent this data by a table, a bar graph, and a line graph.

Reteach
Chapter 1

What you should learn:

1.7	How to identify polygons and parts of polygons and how to discover properties of polygons

Correlation to Pupil's Textbook:

Chapter Test (p. 47)
Exercises 14, 15, 16

Examples | *Identifying Polygons and Discovering Properties of Polygons*

a. Name each polygon shown below.

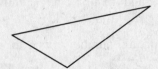

The polygon is an octagon.   The polygon is a triangle.   The polygon is an octagon.

b. Find the total number of diagonals that can be drawn in an octagon.

Use the algebraic model:

Total diagonals	=	Number of vertices	×	Diagonals from each vertex	÷	2

Total number of diagonals $= T$

Numbers of vertices $= n$

Number of diagonals from each vertex $= n - 3$

$$T = n \times (n - 3) \div 2 = \frac{n(n - 3)}{2}$$

For an octagon, $n = 8$. Therefore, $T = \dfrac{8(8 - 3)}{2} = \dfrac{8(5)}{2} = 20$.

Twenty diagonals can be drawn in an octagon.

Guidelines:

- Geometry is the study of shapes, such as polygons, and their measures.
- A polygon is a closed figure that is made up of straight line segments that intersect at their endpoints.
- Each line segment of a polygon is called a side of the polygon.
- Each endpoint of a side of a polygon is called a vertex of the polygon.
- A segment that connects two vertices of a polygon and is not a side is called a diagonal of the polygon.

EXERCISES

In Exercises 1–3, name the polygon.

1.

2.

3.

4. Find the total number of diagonals that can be drawn in a nonagon.

Reteach

Chapter 1

Name _____

| **1.8** | How to use a calculator to discover number patterns and how use diagrams to discover number patterns in real-life situations. |

Correlation to Pupil's Textbook:

Chapter Test (p. 47)
Exercise 13

Examples

Discovering Number Patterns and Discovering Number Patterns in Real Life

a. Use a calculator to calculate the product of 9 and the first nine natural numbers. Describe the pattern.

You are asked to evaluate $9n$, when n is a natural number from 1 to 9.

n	1	2	3	4	5	6	7	8	9
$9n$	9	18	27	36	45	54	63	72	81

From the table, you can see that the tens digit increases by 1 and the units digit decreases by 1.

b. Use the algebraic model given below to find the 9th triangular number.

$$\boxed{\begin{array}{c} n\text{th Triangular} \\ \text{Number} \end{array}} = \boxed{\begin{array}{c} \text{Area of } n\text{-by-}(n+1) \\ \text{rectangle} \end{array}} \div \boxed{2}$$

nth triangular number $= T$

Width of rectangle $= n$

Length of rectangle $= n + 1$

$$T = n \times (n+1) \div 2 = \frac{n(n+1)}{2}$$

For $n = 9$, $T = \dfrac{9(9+1)}{2} = \dfrac{9(10)}{2} = 45$. The 9th triangular number is 45.

Guidelines:

- Numbers have special names, such as whole numbers $(0, 1, 2, 3, \ldots)$, natural numbers $(1, 2, 3, 4, \ldots)$, decimal numbers, and fractions.
- Sequences of numbers often have patterns that can be discovered by using a calculator or a computer.
- The nth triangular number corresponds to half the area of an n-by-$(n+1)$ rectangle.

EXERCISES

In Exercises 1–3, create a table showing your calculations.

1. Calculate the quotient of 240 and each of the first 5 natural numbers.

2. Evaluate $\dfrac{n^2}{3}$ for the first 5 whole numbers.

3. Evaluate $\dfrac{n+1}{n}$ for the first 5 natural numbers. Describe the pattern.

4. Find the 10th triangular number.

Reteach

Chapter 2

What you should learn:

2.1	How to use the Distributive Property and how to use the Distributive Property in real-life problems

Correlation to Pupil's Textbook:

Mid-Chapter Self-Test (p. 69)   **Chapter Test (p. 97)**
Exercises 1–5, 11   Exercises 1, 2, 11

Examples   *Using the Distributive Property and Solving Real-Life Problems*

a. Use the Distributive Property to rewrite each expression.

$$6(n + 3) = 6(n) + 6(3) \quad \textit{Apply Distributive Property.}$$
$$= 6n + 18 \quad \textit{Simplify.}$$

$$10(d + e + f) = 10(d) + 10(e) + 10(f) \quad \textit{Apply Distributive Property.}$$
$$= 10d + 10e + 10f \quad \textit{Simplify.}$$

b. You are helping your grandmother buy flowers for 3 planters. For *each* of the 3 planters, she selects 2 pansies and 4 impatiens and you select 3 petunias. Use the Distributive Property to find the total number of flowers.

Verbal
Model $\boxed{\text{Total}} = 3\,(\,\boxed{\text{pansies}} + \boxed{\text{impatiens}} + \boxed{\text{petunias}}\,)$

Labels   Total number of flowers $= T$
             Number of pansies $= 2$
             Number of impatiens $= 4$
             Number of petunias $= 3$

Algebraic $T = 3(2 + 4 + 3)$
Model
             $= 3(2) + 3(4) + 3(3)$

             $= 6 + 12 + 9$

             $= 27$

You and your grandmother purchased 27 flowers. You can check this result by writing $3(2 + 4 + 3) = 3(9) = 27$.

Guidelines: • The Distributive Property: Let a, b, and c be numbers or variable expressions.

$$a(b + c) = ab + ac \quad \text{and} \quad ab + ac = a(b + c)$$

EXERCISES

In Exercises 1–4, use the Distributive Property to write an equivalent expression. Illustrate your result with an algebra tile sketch.

1. $3(x + 2)$ **2.** $2(x + 1)$ **3.** $4(2x + 3)$ **4.** $5(x + 4)$

In Exercises 5–12, use the Distributive Property to rewrite the expression.

5. $8(11 + 7)$ **6.** $10(r + 6)$ **7.** $1(x + 9)$ **8.** $a(c + 3)$

9. $x(y + z)$ **10.** $5(d + e + 7)$ **11.** $7(2 + e + 5)$ **12.** $p(q + r + s)$

Reteach
Chapter 2

Name _____

What you should learn:

2.2	How to simplify expressions by adding like terms and how to add like terms to simplify expressions in geometry

Correlation to Pupil's Textbook:

Mid-Chapter Self-Test (p. 69)   Chapter Test (p. 97)
Exercises 6–11   Exercises 10, 15, 16
                                 20, 21

Examples *Adding Like Terms and Simplifying Expressions in Geometry*

a. Identify the like terms in the expression.

$4x^2 + 5x + x^2$ *$4x^2$ and x^2 are like terms.*

b. Simplify the expression by adding like terms.

$$2t + 7t^2 + 8t = 2t + 8t + 7t^2 \qquad \textit{Commutative Property}$$
$$= (2+8)t + 7t^2 \qquad \textit{Distributive Property}$$
$$= 10t + 7t^2 \qquad \textit{Simplify.}$$

c. Write an expression that represents the perimeter of the figure shown at the right. Then evaluate the perimeter when $x = \frac{1}{2}, 1, \frac{3}{2}$, and 2. Organize your results in a table and describe the pattern as the values of x increase by $\frac{1}{2}$.

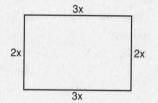

$$\text{Perimeter} = 2x + 3x + 2x + 3x \qquad \textit{Add the side lengths.}$$
$$= (2+3+2+3)x \qquad \textit{Distributive Property}$$
$$= 10x \qquad \textit{Simplify.}$$

Evaluate $10x$ when $x = \frac{1}{2}, 1, \frac{3}{2}$, and 2 and organize the results in a table.

x	$\frac{1}{2}$	1	$\frac{3}{2}$	2
Perimeter	5	10	15	20

The perimeter increases by 5 each time x increases by $\frac{1}{2}$.

Guidelines:

- Two or more terms in an expression are like terms if they have the same variables, raised to the same powers.

- When you add like terms (or collect like terms), the rewritten expression is said to be simplified.

- The Distributive Property can be used to add like terms.

EXERCISES

In Exercises 1–6, simplify the expression.

1. $y^2 + 2z + 3z$ **2.** $a^2 + 2a^2$ **3.** $4(c+d) + (c+d)$

4. $(p+q) + 2(p+q)$ **5.** $10xy + 3xy$ **6.** $7(x+5) + 2x + 1$

Reteach
Chapter 2

Name _____

Examples | *Checking Solutions and Solving Equations with Mental Math*

a. Decide whether $x = 3$ is a solution of the equation $5x - 10 = 4$.

$5x - 10 = 4$	*Write original equation.*
$5(3) - 10 \stackrel{?}{=} 4$	*Substitute 3 for x.*
$15 - 10 \stackrel{?}{=} 4$	*Simplify.*
$5 \neq 4$	$x = 3$ *is not a solution.*

b. Solve the equation with Mental Math.

Equation	Stated as a Question	Solution
$x - 9 = 11$	What number can 9 be subtracted from to obtain 11?	$x = 20$

c. Write the following question as an equation, then solve it mentally.

What number can be multiplied by 12 to obtain 2?

Let x be the number. The equation is $12x = 2$. The number $\frac{1}{6}$ can be multiplied by 12 to obtain 2.

Guidelines:

- An equation states that two expressions are equivalent.
- An identity is an equation that is true for all values of the variables that it contains.
- A conditional equation is not true for all values of the variables that it contains.
- The values that make a conditional equation true are called solutions of the equation.
- Two equations are equivalent if they have the same solutions.

EXERCISES

In Exercises 1–4, decide whether $x = 2$ is a solution of the equation. If it is not, use mental math to find the solution.

1. $16x = 48$ **2.** $18 - x = 16$ **3.** $\dfrac{8}{x} = \dfrac{1}{4}$ **4.** $5x + x = 12$

In Exercises 5–12, solve the equation using mental math. Check your solution.

5. $n + 4 = 15$ **6.** $13 - a = 12$ **7.** $3n = 18$ **8.** $\dfrac{x}{7} = 2$

9. $b - 4 = 5$ **10.** $12y = 36$ **11.** $\dfrac{24}{x} = 8$ **12.** $19 + t = 26$

Name _____

What you should learn:

2.4	How to use addition or subtraction to solve an equation and how to use equations as algebraic models to solve real-life problems

Correlation to Pupil's Textbook:

Mid-Chapter Self-Test (p. 69)   **Chapter Test (p. 97)**
Exercises 15–20   Exercises 4, 5

Examples   *Using Addition or Subtraction and Modeling Real-Life with Equations*

a. Solve the equation showing each step of the solution.

$$n + 18 = 37 \qquad \textit{Original equation}$$
$$n + 18 - 18 = 37 - 18 \qquad \textit{Subtract 18 from both sides.}$$
$$n = 19 \qquad \textit{Simplify.}$$

b. You want to purchase a compact disc for $15.79 (including sales tax), but you have only $11.75. How much money do you need to save before you can purchase the compact disc?

Verbal
Model

Money you have	+	Money you must save	=	Price of compact disc

Labels
    Money you have $= 11.75$ (dollars)
    Money you must save $= x$ (dollars)
    Price of compact disc $= 15.79$ (dollars)

Algebraic
Model

$$11.75 + x = 15.79$$
$$11.75 + x - 11.75 = 15.79 - 11.75$$
$$x + 11.75 - 11.75 = 15.79 - 11.75$$
$$x = 4.04$$

You need to save $4.04. You can check this result by noting that
$11.75 + 4.04 = 15.79$.

Guidelines:

- Addition and Subtraction Properties of Equality: Adding the same number to both sides of an equation or subtracting the same number from both sides of an equation produces an equivalent equation.
- Properties of Addition and Multiplication:
  Commutative Property of Addition: $a + b = b + a$
  Commutative Property of Multiplication: $ab = ba$
  Associative Property of Addition: $a + (b + c) = (a + b) + c$
  Associative Property of Multiplication: $a(bc) = (ab)c$

EXERCISES

In Exercises 1–6, solve the equation and check your solution.

1. $f + 34 = 76$ **2.** $h - 124 = 102$ **3.** $457 = k + 79$

4. $x - 3.4 = 15$ **5.** $45.6 = z + 22.4$ **6.** $86 = w - 25.8$

Reteach
Chapter 2

Name _____

What you should learn:

2.5	How to use multiplication or division to solve an equation and how to use equations to solve real-life problems	

Correlation to Pupil's Textbook:

Chapter Test (p. 97)

Exercises 3, 6

Examples | *Using Multiplication or Division and Modeling Real-Life Situations*

a. Solve the equation, using multiplication.

$\dfrac{k}{6} = 11$ *Original equation*

$6 \cdot \dfrac{k}{6} = 6 \cdot 11$ *Multiply both sides by 6.*

$k = 66$ *Simplify.*

b. You are ordering lunch at a fast-food restaurant. You order 4 burgers and the total price is $2.52 (including tax). What is the price of each burger?

Verbal Model	$\boxed{\text{Number of burgers}}$ · $\boxed{\text{Price per burger}}$ = $\boxed{\text{Total price}}$

Labels   Number of burgers $= 4$

                 Price per burger $= x$ (dollars)

                 Total price $= 2.52$ (dollars)

Algebraic Model

$4x = 2.52$ *Original equation*

$\dfrac{4x}{4} = \dfrac{2.52}{4}$ *Divide both sides by 4.*

$x = 0.63$ *Simplify.*

The price of each burger is $.63 (including tax). You can check this by multiplying to see that $4(0.63) = 2.52$.

Guidelines:

- Multiplication and Division Properties of Equality: Multiplying both sides of an equation by the same nonzero number or dividing both sides of an equation by the same nonzero number produces an equivalent equation.
- To simplify a fraction that has a common factor in its numerator and denominator, factor the numerator and denominator, divide each by the common factor, then simplify.
- When solving real-life problems that involve division, check to see that the units of measure make sense.

EXERCISES

In Exercises 1–8, solve the equation. Check your solution.

1. $8x = 96$ **2.** $98 = 7n$ **3.** $\dfrac{g}{3} = 34$ **4.** $21 = \dfrac{k}{5}$

5. $211.5 = 5a$ **6.** $\dfrac{y}{2.7} = 6$ **7.** $\dfrac{q}{1} = 55$ **8.** $8.1z = 56.7$

Reteach
Chapter 2

Name _____

What you should learn:

2.6	How to translate verbal phrases into algebraic expressions and how to model real-life situations with algebraic expressions

Correlation to Pupil's Textbook:

Chapter Test (p. 97)

Exercises 12–14

Examples   *Translating Verbal Phrases and Modeling Real-Life Phrases*

a. Translate each verbal phrase into an algebraic expression.

Eleven more than a number $\quad n + 11$

Eight less than a number $\quad x - 8$

b. The following verbal phrase contains two number operations. Use labels to translate the phrase into an algebraic expression.

The product of a number and 4 $\qquad$ Labels: n is a number. $\qquad n(4m)$
times another number $\qquad\qquad\qquad\qquad\qquad$ m is another number.

c. You are renting computer games and video movies. The rental charge for each game is $2.50 and the rental charge for each movie is $3.00. Write an algebraic expression that represents your total rental charge. Then use the expression to find the total charge for renting 2 games and 3 movies.

Verbal Model	Rental charge per game	$\cdot$	Number of games	$+$	Rental charge per movie	$\cdot$	Number of movies

Labels $\qquad$ Rental charge per game $= 2.50$ $\qquad$ (dollars per game)
$\qquad\qquad$ Number of games $= g$ $\qquad\qquad\quad$ (games)
$\qquad\qquad$ Rental charge per movie $= 3.00$ $\qquad$ (dollars per movie)
$\qquad\qquad$ Number of movies $= m$ $\qquad\qquad\;$ (movies)

Algebraic $\qquad 2.50g + 3.00m$
Model

The total charge for renting 2 games and 3 movies is as follows.

Total charge $= 2.50g + 3.00m \qquad$ *Algebraic expression*

$\qquad\qquad\quad = 2.50(2) + 3.00(3) \qquad$ *Substitute 2 for g and 3 for m.*

$\qquad\qquad\quad = \$14.00 \qquad$ *Simplify.*

Guidelines: $\quad \bullet$ When translating verbal phrases into algebraic expressions, look for words that indicate a number operation.

EXERCISES

In Exercises 1–4, translate the verbal phrase into an algebraic expression.

1. The sum of 4 and 6 times another number.

2. The difference of 30 and twice a number.

3. The quotient of a number and 4 more than another number.

4. 15 minus the product of 9 and a number.

What you should learn:

2.7	How to translate verbal sentences into algebraic equations and how to model real-life situations with algebraic equations

Correlation to Pupil's Textbook:

Chapter Test (p. 97)
Exercises 18, 19

Examples | *Translating Verbal Sentences and Modeling Real-Life Sentences*

a. State whether each quantity is an expression or an equation. Solve or simplify.

$s - 16 = 18$ $s - 16 = 18$ is an equation.   The solution is $s = 34$.

$x + 8x - 4$ $x + 8x - 4$ is an expression.   A simpler expression is $9x - 4$.

b. Write an algebraic equation that represents the verbal sentence. Then solve the equation.

The sum of 35 and t is 49. $35 + t = 49$ $t = 14$

c. An automobile is traveling 21 miles per hour faster than a school bus. The school bus is traveling at a speed of 33 miles per hour. What is the speed of the automobile?

Verbal
Model $\boxed{\text{Speed of automobile}} = \boxed{\text{Speed of school bus}} + 21$

Labels   Speed of automobile $= s$ (miles per hour)
           Speed of school bus $= 33$ (miles per hour)

Algebraic $s = 33 + 21$ *Algebraic equation*
Model $s = 54$ *Simplify.*

The speed of the automobile is 54 miles per hour. You can check this by noting that 54 is 21 more than 33.

Guidelines:

- The algebraic model for a sentence is an equation.
- You can solve an equation, but you cannot solve an expression.

EXERCISES

In Exercises 1–4, match the sentence with an equation.

a. $\dfrac{n}{4} = 8$ **b.** $4n = 8$ **c.** $n + 4 = 8$ **d.** $4 - n = 8$

1. The difference of 4 and n is 8.   **2.** 4 times n is 8.

3. The quotient of n and 4 is 8.   **4.** 4 more than n is 8.

In Exercises 5–8, write a verbal sentence that represents the equation.

5. $d + 35 = 43$ **6.** $\dfrac{q}{6} = 12$ **7.** $67 = t - 7$ **8.** $3.4w = 27.2$

Reteach
Chapter 2

What you should learn:

| 2.8 | How to use a systematic problem-solving plan and how to use other problem-solving strategies |

Example — Using a Problem-Solving Plan and Using Other Problem-Solving Strategies

You are working on a scouting badge. You need 60 points on 4 projects to earn the badge. On your first project, you earn 24 points. On the second project, you earn 14 points. On the third project, you earn 12 points. How many more points do you need on the fourth project to complete the badge?

Verbal Model

| Points on project 1 | + | Points on project 2 | + | Points on project 3 | + | Points on project 4 | = | Total points |

Labels
Points on project 1 = 24
Points on project 2 = 14
Points on project 3 = 12
Points on project 4 = p
Total points = 60

Algebraic Model

$$24 + 14 + 12 + p = 60$$
$$50 + p = 60$$
$$p = 10$$

You need 10 points on the fourth project to complete the badge.

Guidelines:

- A General Problem-Solving Plan:

  1. Write a verbal model that will give you what you need to know to solve the problem.
  2. Assign labels to each part of your verbal model.
  3. Write an algebraic model based on your verbal model.
  4. Solve the algebraic model.
  5. Answer the original question.
  6. Check that your answer is reasonable.

- Other problem-solving strategies include "solving a simpler problem," and "guess, check, and revise."

EXERCISE

You are an automobile salesperson. Your monthly earnings consist of your base salary and your sales bonus. Your bonus is one-fiftieth of the amount of your monthly sales. Your monthly base salary is $5000 and you sell $200,000 this month. How much do you earn this month?

Reteach
Chapter 2

Name _____

What you should learn:

2.9	How to solve simple inequalities and how to use inequalities to solve real-life problems

Correlation to Pupil's Textbook:

Chapter Test (p. 97)
Exercises 7–9, 17

Examples | *Solving Simple Inequalities and Modeling Real Life with Inequalities*

a. Write an inequality that represents each sentence.

s minus 6 is less than 78. $\qquad\qquad\qquad$ $s - 6 < 78$

12 is greater than or equal to the sum of k and 3. $\quad$ $12 \geq k + 3$

b. Solve the inequality.

$3 \leq \dfrac{r}{16}$ $\qquad\qquad$ *Original inequality*

$3 \cdot 16 \leq \dfrac{r}{16} \cdot 16$ $\qquad$ *Multiply each side by 16.*

$48 \leq r$ $\qquad\qquad$ *Solution of inequality*

c. Your grade in geography is based on a total of 350 points for 4 tests. To earn a B, you need 287 points. Your first three test scores are 82, 76, and 91. How many additional points must you earn on the fourth test in order to earn a B?

Verbal
Model

$$\boxed{\begin{array}{c}\text{Test 1} \\ \text{points}\end{array}} + \boxed{\begin{array}{c}\text{Test 2} \\ \text{points}\end{array}} + \boxed{\begin{array}{c}\text{Test 3} \\ \text{points}\end{array}} + \boxed{\begin{array}{c}\text{Test 4} \\ \text{points}\end{array}} \geq 287$$

Labels
$\qquad$ Test 1 points $= 82$
$\qquad$ Test 2 points $= 76$
$\qquad$ Test 3 points $= 91$
$\qquad$ Test 4 points $= p$

Algebraic
Model
$\qquad 82 + 76 + 91 + p \geq 287$
$\qquad\qquad 249 + p \geq 287$
$\qquad\qquad\qquad p \geq 38$

You must earn at least 38 points on the fourth test in order to earn a B.

Guidelines:

- Finding all solutions of an inequality is called solving the inequality.
- To solve an inequality:
  1. You can add or subtract the same number from each side.
  2. You can multiply or divide both sides by the same positive number.

EXERCISES

In Exercises 1–6, solve the inequality.

1. $c - 4 < 51$ $\qquad\qquad$ **2.** $12x \leq 156$ $\qquad\qquad$ **3.** $\dfrac{t}{8} > 3.8$

4. $y + 47 \geq 86$ $\qquad\qquad$ **5.** $48 > 5s$ $\qquad\qquad$ **6.** $\dfrac{w}{3.5} < 14$

Reteach
Chapter 3

Name _____

What you should learn:

3.1	How to model integers on a number line and how to find the absolute value of a number

Correlation to Pupil's Textbook:

Mid-Chapter Self-Test (p. 120)
Exercises 1–6, 15

Chapter Test (p. 143)
Exercises 1–5

Examples	*Integers and the Number Line and Finding the Absolute Value of a Number*

a. The following numbers are called integers.

$$\ldots, -3, -2, -1, 0, 1, 2, 3, \ldots$$

Draw a number line and plot the integers -3 and 3.

Solution: Draw a dot at the point that represents each integer on the number line. Plot -3 to the left of 3 since $-3 < 3$.

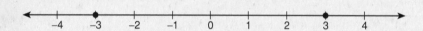

b. Two numbers that have the same absolute value but opposite signs are called opposites. Draw a number line and plot the integer -5 and the opposite of -5.

Draw a dot at the point -5. The opposite of -5 is 5. Draw a dot at the point 5. Note that $|-5| = |5| = 5$.

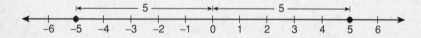

Guidelines:

- If a and b are integers, then the inequality $a < b$ means that a lies to the left of b on the number line.

- Absolute values are written with two vertical rules, $|\quad|$, called absolute value signs.

- The absolute value of a number cannot be negative because absolute value is a distance which cannot be negative.

EXERCISES

In Exercises 1–4, draw a number line and plot the integers.

1. $7, 1, -2$ **2.** $0, 5, -3$ **3.** $-3, -1, -4$ **4.** $-2, 4, -6$

In Exercises 5–8, write the opposite and absolute value of the integer.

5. -5 _____   **6.** 14 **7.** -15 **8.** 33

Reteach

Chapter 3

Name _____

What you should learn:

3.2	How to add two integers and how to use integer addition to solve real-life problems

Correlation to Pupil's Textbook:

Mid-Chapter Self-Test (p. 120)   **Chapter Test (p. 143)**
Exercises 7–10, 12   Exercise 7

Examples — Adding Two Integers and Solving Real-Life Problems

a. To add two integers with the same sign, add their absolute values and write the common sign.

Add -12 and -4. $-12 + (-4) = -16$ The sum of two negative integers is negative.

Add 7 and 8. $7 + 8 = 15$ The sum of two positive integers is positive.

b. To add two integers with opposite signs, subtract the smaller absolute value from the larger absolute value and write the sign of the integer with the greater absolute value.

Add -5 and 3.   Subtract 3 from -5 and write $(-5) + 3 = -2$
the sign of -5.

c. The price of gasoline was $1.03 per gallon in March. In April, the price was $1.01 per gallon. Write an addition equation that relates the gasoline prices in March and April.

From March to April, the price dropped $0.02. This can be represented by adding (-0.02) to the March price.

$$\boxed{\begin{array}{c}\text{March}\\\text{price}\end{array}} + \boxed{\begin{array}{c}\text{Price drop}\\\text{of }(-0.02)\end{array}} = \boxed{\begin{array}{c}\text{April}\\\text{price}\end{array}}$$

$$1.03 + (-0.02) = 1.01$$

Guidelines:

- The sum of two positive integers is positive.
- The sum of two negative integers is negative.
- The sum of any two opposites is zero.

EXERCISES

In Exercises 1–8, find the sum. Write your conclusion as an equation.

1. $-9 + 12$ **2.** $5 + (-14)$ **3.** $7 + 11$ **4.** $0 + (-17)$

5. $-23 + 4$ **6.** $-11 + (-13)$ **7.** $6 + 0$ **8.** $8 + (-8)$

What you should learn:

3.3	How to add three or more integers and how to simplify expressions by adding like terms

Correlation to Pupil's Textbook:

Chapter Test (p. 143)
Exercises 14, 16–20

Examples	*Adding Three or More Integers and Adding Like Terms*

a. Add -4, 6, and 5 on a number line.

On the number line, adding a positive number is represented by movement to the right. Begin at -4, move 6 units to the right, then move 5 units to the right. Because you end at 7, you conclude that $-4 + 6 + 5 = 7$.

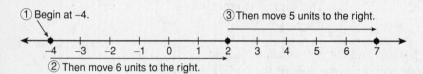

b. Add -5, -3, and 2 on a number line.

On the number line, adding a negative number is represented by movement to the left. Begin at -5, move 3 units to the left, then move 2 units to the right. Because you end at -6, you conclude that $-5 + (-3) + 2 = -6$.

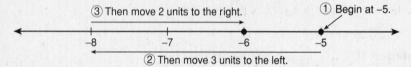

c. Simplify the expression $12x + (-4x) + (-6x)$ by adding like terms. Then evaluate the expression when $x = 5$.

When you add like terms, you can add the coefficients.

$12x + (-4x) + (-6x) = [12 + (-4) + (-6)]x = 2x$

When $x = 5$, the value of the expression is $2x = 2(5) = 10$.

Guidelines:

- In the expression $-6n + 3$, the number -6 is the coefficient of n.
- When you add like terms, you apply the Distributive Property to the coefficients of the terms, then simplify.

EXERCISES

In Exercises 1–3, find the sum. Write your conclusion as an equation.

1. $-8 + 3 + 7$

2. $5 + (-3) + (-9)$

3. $13 + 4 + (-5)$

In Exercises 4–6, simplify the expression. Then evaluate the expression when $x = 3$.

4. $-4x + 9x + 7$

5. $7x + (-2) + (-12x) + 5$

6. $3x + (-11x) + 9x$

Reteach

Chapter 3

What you should learn:

3.4	How to use opposites to subtract integers and how to simplify expressions involving subtraction

Correlation to Pupil's Textbook:

Mid-Chapter Self-Test (p. 120)   **Chapter Test (p. 143)**

Exercises 11, 13   Exercise 8

Examples   *Subtracting Integers and Simplifying Expressions*

a. To subtract an integer b from an integer a, add its opposite.

$4 - 9 = 4 + (-9) = -5$ Opposite of 9 is -9.

$-8 - (-5) = -8 + 5 = -3$ Opposite of (-5) is 5.

$15 - 6 = 15 + (-6) = 9$ Opposite of 6 is (-6).

$-10 - 5 = -10 + (-5) = -15$ Opposite of 5 is (-5).

b. To recognize the terms of an expression involving subtraction, you can rewrite the expression as a sum.

Rewrite $5x - x - 3$ as a sum. $5x - x - 3 = 5x + (-1x) + (-3)$

Identify the terms of the expression.   The terms are $5x$, $-1x$, and -3.

c. The "subtraction form" of the Distributive Property is $a(b - c) = ab - ac$.

Use the Distributive Property to simplify the expression $9x - 4x - 5$. Then evaluate the expression when $x = 4$.

$9x - 4x - 5 = (9 - 4)x - 5$ *Distributive Property*

$\qquad\qquad\quad = 5x - 5$ *Simplify.*

When $x = 4$, the value of the expression is $5x - 5 = 5(4) - 5 = 15$.

Guidelines:

- The number you obtain from subtracting one integer from another is the difference of the integers.
- If b is positive, then its opposite $-b$ is negative.
- If b is negative, then its opposite $-b$ is positive.
- The terms of an algebraic expression are separated by addition, not subtraction.

EXERCISES

In Exercises 1–8, find the difference. Write your conclusion as an equation.

1. $11 - 16$ **2.** $24 - (-3)$ **3.** $-18 - 9$ **4.** $-15 - (-4)$

5. $0 - 33$ **6.** $35 - 6$ **7.** $0 - (-13)$ **8.** $-5 - 5$

In Exercises 9–11, rewrite the expression as a sum. Then identify the terms of the expression.

9. $3n - 5n + m$ **10.** $8x - 3x - 4$ **11.** $7a - 9b - 6$

In Exercises 12–14, simplify the expression. Then evaluate the expression when $x = 2$.

12. $-16x - (-5x) + 8$ **13.** $-12x - 7x + 10$ **14.** $2x - (-2x)$

Reteach
Chapter 3

What you should learn:

3.5	How to multiply integers and how to use integer multiplication to model real-life problems

Correlation to Pupil's Textbook:

Chapter Test (p. 143)
Exercises 9, 10

Examples *Multiplying Integers and Modeling Real-Life Situations*

a. Multiply 6 and 3. $6(3) = 18$ The product of two positive numbers is positive.

Multiply -5 and -7. $(-5)(-7) = 35$ The product of two negative numbers is positive.

Multiply 4 and -11. $4(-11) = -44$ The product of a positive and a negative number is negative.

b. Evaluate $-x^2$ when $x = 5$.

The order of operations for powers and for negative signs is that the power is evaluated before the negative sign.

$$-x^2 = -(x)(x) = -(5)(5) = -25$$

c. To convert from a Fahrenheit temperature to a Celsius temperature, subtract 32 from the Fahrenheit temperature and multiply by $\frac{5}{9}$. Write an algebraic model for this relationship. Then use the model to find the Celsius temperature that corresponds to $-13°$ F.

Verbal
Model $\boxed{\begin{array}{c}\text{Celsius} \\ \text{temperature}\end{array}} = \left(\boxed{\begin{array}{c}\text{Fahrenheit} \\ \text{temperature}\end{array}} - 32 \right) \frac{5}{9}$

Labels   Celsius temperature $= C$ (degrees C)
          Fahrenheit temperature $= F$ (degrees F)

Algebraic
Model $C = (F - 32)\frac{5}{9}$

The Celsius temperature that corresponds to $-13°$ F is

$C = (F - 32)\frac{5}{9}$ *Write model.*

$\quad = (-13 - 32)\frac{5}{9}$ *Substitute -13 for F.*

$\quad = (-45)\frac{5}{9}$ *Simplify.*

$\quad = -25°C.$ *Simplify.*

Guidelines: • The order of operations for powers and for negative signs applies to expressions that have variables (the power of a variable is evaluated before the negative sign).

EXERCISES

In Exercises 1–4, find the product. Write your conclusion as an equation.

1. $4(-5)$ **2.** $(-9)(-8)$ **3.** $-10 \cdot 2$ **4.** $15(1)$

In Exercises 5–8, evaluate the expression when $x = -2$ and $y = -3$.

5. xy **6.** $x^2(y)$ **7.** xy^2 **8.** $-x^2$

Reteach
Chapter 3

Name _____

What you should learn:

3.6	How to divide integers and how to use integer division to model real-life problems

Correlation to Pupil's Textbook:

Chapter Test (p. 143)
Exercises 6, 11, 12, 19–21

Examples *Dividing Integers and Modeling Real-Life Problems*

a. Divide 15 by 5. $\dfrac{15}{5} = 3$ The quotient of two positive numbers is positive.

Divide -28 by -7. $\dfrac{-28}{-7} = 4$ The quotient of two negative numbers is positive.

Divide 18 by -9. $\dfrac{18}{-9} = -2$ The quotient of a positive and a negative number is negative.

b. The local weather station recorded the following daily low temperatures (in degrees Fahrenheit) over a 12-day period during the month of January.

$$-4, \ -2, \ -5, \ 0, \ 2, \ -7, \ -6, \ 4, \ 5, \ 7, \ -1, \ -5$$

What was the average daily low temperature (in degrees Fahrenheit) for the 12-day period?

Verbal Model $\boxed{\begin{array}{c}\text{Average daily} \\ \text{low temperature}\end{array}} = \dfrac{\boxed{\text{Sum of temperatures above and below zero}}}{12}$

Labels   Average daily low temperature $= A$ (degrees Fahrenheit)
Sum of temperatures above and below zero $= -12$ (degrees Fahrenheit)

Algebraic Model $A = \dfrac{-4 + (-2) + (-5) + 0 + 2 + (-7) + (-6) + 4 + 5 + 7 + (-1) + (-5)}{12}$

$= \dfrac{-12}{12} = -1$

The average daily low temperature was $-1°$F.

Guidelines:
- You cannot divide a number by 0.
- When 0 is divided by a nonzero number, the result is 0.
- To find the average (or mean) of n numbers, add the numbers and divide the result by n.

EXERCISES

In Exercises 1–8, evaluate the expression. Check your result by multiplying.

1. $\dfrac{66}{3}$ **2.** $\dfrac{120}{-8}$ **3.** $\dfrac{-144}{9}$ **4.** $\dfrac{-170}{-34}$

5. $0/-26$ **6.** $297 \div 27$ **7.** $-525 \div (-35)$ **8.** $338/(-13)$

In Exercises 9–10, find the average of the numbers.

9. $-8, \ -5, \ 4, \ 13, \ -12, \ -4$ **10.** $-15, \ -6, \ -23, \ 0, \ -11$

Reteach
Chapter 3

Name _____

Correlation to Pupil's Textbook:
Chapter Test (p. 143)
Exercises 16–18

What you should learn:

3.7	How to solve equations involving integers and how to use integer operations to model real-life problems

---

Examples	*Solving Equations and Modeling Real-Life Problems*

a. Solve each equation, using the opposite operation to isolate the variable.

$$n + 7 = 3 \qquad \textit{Original equation}$$
$$n + 7 - 7 = 3 - 7 \qquad \textit{Subtract 7 from each side.}$$
$$n = -4 \qquad \textit{Simplify.}$$

$$-18 = x - 5 \qquad \textit{Original equation}$$
$$-18 + 5 = x - 5 + 5 \qquad \textit{Add 5 to each side.}$$
$$-13 = x \qquad \textit{Simplify.}$$

b. You are planning a picnic for your school's marching band. The expenses will be $240 for food and $25 for renting the picnic shelter. You will charge $5 per person. Will your band make a profit if 50 members attend?

The profit is the difference between total income and total expenses.

Verbal Model:
$$\boxed{\text{Profit}} = \boxed{\begin{array}{c}\text{Picnic}\\\text{charge}\end{array}} \cdot \boxed{\begin{array}{c}\text{Number of}\\\text{members}\end{array}} - \boxed{\text{Expenses}}$$

Labels
- Profit $= P$ (dollars)
- Picnic charge $= 5$ (dollars per member)
- Number of members attending $= n$ (people)
- Expenses $= 240 + 25 = 265$ (dollars)

Algebraic Model $P = 5n - 265$

If 50 members attend, then the profit is $P = 5(50) - 265 = -15$. Your band would have a loss of $15.

Guidelines:
- Addition and subtraction are opposite operations, and multiplication and division are inverse operations.
- To isolate n, you should perform the inverse (or opposite) operations from those involved in the equation.

EXERCISES

In Exercises 1–8, solve the equation. Check your solution.

1. $d + 7 = -4$ **2.** $y - 17 = -6$ **3.** $54 = -9x$ **4.** $\dfrac{c}{15} = -3$

5. $-35 = k - 5$ **6.** $6 = -12t$ **7.** $-10 = \dfrac{q}{-2}$ **8.** $19 = w + 22$

What you should learn:

| 3.8 | How to plot points in a coordinate plane and how to use a coordinate plane to represent data graphically |

Correlation to Pupil's Textbook:

Chapter Test (p. 143)

Exercises 13–15

| **Examples** | *Points in a Coordinate Plane and Representing Data Graphically* |

a. A coordinate plane is shown at the right. It has two number lines that intersect at a right angle. Label each of the following.

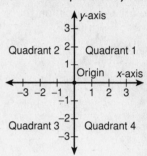

Origin – the point of intersection of the two number lines

x-axis – the horizontal number line

y-axis – the vertical number line

Quadrants 1, 2, 3, 4 – four parts of the coordinate plane

b. Each point in a coordinate plane can be represented by an ordered pair of numbers, (x, y). Match each ordered pair with its corresponding point in the coordinate plane shown at the right. Identify the quadrant in which the point lies.

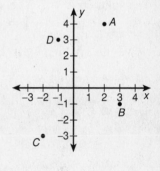

1. $(3, -1)$ B, Quadrant 4

2. $(-1, 3)$ D, Quadrant 2

3. $(2, 4)$ A, Quadrant 1

4. $(-2, -3)$ C, Quadrant 3

c. An ordered pair (x, y) is a solution of an equation involving x and y if the equation is true when the values of x and y are substituted into the equation. Show that the ordered pair $(-3, 5)$ is a solution of the equation $x + 2y = 7$. Then find two other solutions.

Equation	Solution	Check
$x + 2y = 7$	$(-3, 5)$	$-3 + 2(5) = 7$
$x + 2y = 7$	$(-1, 4)$	$-1 + 2(4) = 7$
$x + 2y = 7$	$(1, 3)$	$1 + 2(3) = 7$

Guidelines:

- The first number of an ordered pair is the x-coordinate and it gives the position of the point relative to the x-axis.
- The second number of an ordered pair is the y-coordinate and it gives the position of the point relative to the y-axis.
- Locating the point in the coordinate plane that corresponds to an ordered pair is called plotting the point.

EXERCISES

In Exercises 1–4, plot the point on a single coordinate plane. Determine the quadrant in which the point lies.

1. $A(-5, 4)$ 2. $B(3, -2)$ 3. $C(-2, 3)$ 4. $D(-1, -2)$

Name _____

What you should learn:

Correlation to Pupil's Textbook:

| **4.1** | How to use two transformations to solve an equation |

Mid-Chapter Self-Test (p. 167)   **Chapter Test (p. 191)**
Exercises 6–11, 16, 17, 20   Exercises 1, 2, 11

| **Examples** | *Using Two Transformations to Solve an Equation* |

a. Solve the equation by isolating the variable.

$$-4x - 1 = 11$$ *Original equation*

$$-4x - 1 + 1 = 11 + 1$$ *To isolate the x-term, add 1 to each side.*

$$-4x = 12$$ *Simplify.*

$$\frac{-4x}{-4} = \frac{12}{-4}$$ *To isolate x, divide each side by −4.*

$$x = -3$$ *Simplify.*

The solution is -3. The solution checks in the original equation because
$-4(-3) - 1 = 12 - 1 = 11$.

b. Solve the equation by isolating the variable.

$$\frac{z}{3} + 1 = -4$$ *Original equation*

$$\frac{z}{3} + 1 - 1 = -4 - 1$$ *To isolate the z term, subtract 1 from each side.*

$$\frac{z}{3} = -5$$ *Simplify.*

$$3 \cdot \frac{z}{3} = 3(-5)$$ *To isolate z, multiply each side by 3.*

$$z = -15$$ *Simplify.*

The solution is -15. The solution checks because $\frac{-15}{3} + 1 = -5 + 1 = -4$.

Guidelines: • To solve an equation with two transformations:

    1. Simplify both sides of the equation (if needed).

    2. Use inverse operations to isolate the variable.

EXERCISES

In Exercises 1–6, solve the equation. Check your solution.

1. $6x - 1 = 17$ **2.** $-4y + 5 = 21$ **3.** $\frac{f}{2} - 7 = 8$

4. $-3x + 1 = -8$ **5.** $-5w - 1 = -21$ **6.** $\frac{m}{-8} + 4 = -3$

Reteach
Chapter 4

Name _____

What you should learn:

| 4.2 | How to use three or more transformations to solve an equation and how to solve real-life problems using multi-step equations |

Correlation to Pupil's Textbook:

Mid-Chapter Self-Test (p. 167)   Chapter Test (p. 191)
Exercises 12–14, 18   Exercise 4

Examples   *Solving Multi-Step Equations and Solving Real-Life Problems*

a. Solve the equation $8x - 7x - 4 = 2$ by combining like terms before applying inverse operations.

$$8x - 7x - 4 = 2 \qquad \textit{Rewrite original equation.}$$
$$x - 4 = 2 \qquad \textit{Combine like terms: } 8x - 7x = x.$$
$$x - 4 + 4 = 2 + 4 \qquad \textit{Add 4 to each side.}$$
$$x = 6 \qquad \textit{Simplify.}$$

The solution is 6. Check this in the original equation.

b. Your basketball team is selling programs for $1 per program. To print the programs, the printer charges $80, plus $0.25 per program. How many programs does the team need to sell to make a profit of $250?

Verbal
Model

$$\boxed{\text{Profit}} = \boxed{\text{Income}} - \boxed{\text{Expenses}}$$

$$= 1 \cdot \boxed{\begin{array}{c}\text{Number of}\\\text{programs}\end{array}} - \left(80 + 0.25 \cdot \boxed{\begin{array}{c}\text{Number of}\\\text{programs}\end{array}}\right)$$

Labels   Number of programs $= n$

Algebraic $250 = 1n - (80 + 0.25n)$
Model
$$250 = 1n - 80 - 0.25n$$
$$250 = 0.75n - 80$$
$$330 = 0.75n$$
$$440 = n$$

The team needs to sell 440 programs to make a profit of $250.

Guidelines:

- Before applying inverse operations to solve an equation, you should simplify by combining any like terms.
- You should check your solution in the original equation.

EXERCISES

In Exercises 1–6, solve the equation. Check your solution.

1. $-9x + 3x + 5 = -1$ **2.** $10x - 14 - x = -5$ **3.** $-12 = 5t - 7t + 6$

4. $\frac{7}{3}x - \frac{1}{3}x - 7 = 1$ **5.** $11a - 5a - 8a = 18$ **6.** $6 = -5x - 2x - 8$

7. Use the model in Example b above to find the number of programs the team needs to sell to make a profit of $400.

Reteach
Chapter 4

Name _____

What you should learn:

4.3	How to solve an equation by multiplying by a reciprocal and how to write two-step equations that model real-life problems

Correlation to Pupil's Textbook:

Mid-Chapter Self-Test (p. 167) **Chapter Test (p. 191)**
Exercises 1–5   Exercises 9, 10

Examples	*Using Reciprocals and Writing Real-Life Models*

a. Solve the equation by multiplying by a reciprocal.

$$-\tfrac{1}{3}x = 4 \qquad \textit{Original equation}$$
$$-3 \cdot \left(-\tfrac{1}{3}\right)x = -3 \cdot 4 \qquad \textit{Multiply each side by } -3.$$
$$x = -12 \qquad \textit{Simplify.}$$

b. The width of a rectangular garden is 4 feet less than its length. Write a model for the perimeter of the garden. Use the model to find the dimensions of the garden if you know that the perimeter is 52 feet.

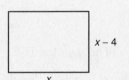

Verbal Model

Perimeter of garden	=	Length	+	Width	+	Length	+	Width

Labels   Length = x
          Width = $x - 4$

Algebraic Model

$$52 = x + (x - 4) + x + (x - 4)$$
$$52 = 4x - 8$$
$$60 = 4x$$
$$\tfrac{1}{4} \cdot 60 = \tfrac{1}{4} \cdot 4x$$
$$15 = x$$

The length of the garden is 15 feet and the width of the garden is $15 - 4 = 11$ feet.

Guidelines:
- Multiplying by the reciprocal of a number produces the same result as dividing by the number.
- When you multiply a number by its reciprocal, you obtain 1.

EXERCISES

In Exercises 1–4, find the reciprocal of the number.

1. 13   **2.** $-\tfrac{1}{6}$ **3.** -4 **4.** $\tfrac{1}{2}$

In Exercises 5–7, solve the equation.

5. $-\tfrac{1}{3}x + 4 = -5$ **6.** $-18q - 12 = 24$ **7.** $\tfrac{1}{4}w - 6 = 2$

8. Use the model in Example b above to find the dimensions of a garden with a perimeter of 28 feet.

Name _____

What you should learn:

4.4 How to use the Distributive Property to solve equations

Examples *Using the Distributive Property*

a. Solve $6(x + 3) - 2x = 14$.

$$6(x + 3) - 2x = 14 \qquad \textit{Rewrite original equation.}$$
$$6x + 18 - 2x = 14 \qquad \textit{Distributive Property}$$
$$4x + 18 = 14 \qquad \textit{Combine like terms.}$$
$$4x + 18 - 18 = 14 - 18 \qquad \textit{Subtract 18 from each side.}$$
$$4x = -4 \qquad \textit{Simplify.}$$
$$\frac{4x}{4} = \frac{-4}{4} \qquad \textit{Divide each side by 4.}$$
$$x = -1 \qquad \textit{Simplify.}$$

The solution is -1. Check this in the original equation.

b. Use the Distributive Property and then solve $-43 = \frac{1}{5}(x - 15)$.

$$-43 = \frac{1}{5}(x - 15) \qquad \textit{Original equation}$$
$$-43 = \frac{1}{5}x - \frac{1}{5}(15) \qquad \textit{Distributive Property}$$
$$-43 = \frac{1}{5}x - 3 \qquad \textit{Simplify.}$$
$$-43 + 3 = \frac{1}{5}x - 3 + 3 \qquad \textit{Add 3 to each side.}$$
$$-40 = \frac{1}{5}x \qquad \textit{Simplify.}$$
$$5(-40) = 5\left(\frac{1}{5}x\right) \qquad \textit{Multiply each side by 5.}$$
$$-200 = x \qquad \textit{Simplify.}$$

Guidelines: • To solve an equation:

     1. Simplify both sides of the equation (if needed).

     2. Use inverse operations to isolate the variable.

EXERCISES

In Exercises 1–6, solve the equation. Check your solution.

1. $5x + 2(x + 3) = 20$
2. $14 = 3(n - 4) - 2n$
3. $-2(z + 3) = 10$

4. $4(s - 3) + s = -17$
5. $\frac{2}{3}y - \frac{1}{3}y + 7 = -2$
6. $5(6 - a) - 8a = 4$

What you should learn:

| 4.5 | How to solve equations with variables on both sides and how to use equations to model problems in geometry |

Correlation to Pupil's Textbook:

Chapter Test (p. 191)
Exercises 5, 7, 8

Examples *Collecting Variables on One Side and Modeling Problems in Geometry*

a. Solve $3x - 4 = 7x + 4$.

$3x - 4 = 7x + 4$	*Rewrite original equation.*
$3x - 4 - 3x = 7x + 4 - 3x$	*Subtract $3x$ from each side.*
$-4 = 4x + 4$	*Simplify.*
$-4 - 4 = 4x + 4 - 4$	*Subtract 4 from each side.*
$-8 = 4x$	*Simplify.*
$\dfrac{-8}{4} = \dfrac{4x}{4}$	*Divide each side by* 4.
$-2 = x$	*Simplify.*

The solution is -2. You can check this result by substituting -2 for x into the original equation.

b. Find the value of x so that the square and the triangle have the same perimeter.

| Square's perimeter | $=$ | Triangle's perimeter | Write verbal model. |

$4(x + 1) = (x + 1) + (x + 2) + (x + 3)$

$4x + 4 = 3x + 6$

$x + 4 = 6$

$x = 2$

When $x = 2$, each figure has a perimeter of 12.

Square labeled $x + 1$ on top and $x + 1$ on side. Triangle labeled $x + 1$, $x + 3$, and $x + 2$.

Guidelines:

- To solve equations with variables on both sides, collect like variables on the same side.
- It is suggested that you collect variables on the side with the term that has the greater variable coefficient.

EXERCISES

In Exercises 1–6, solve the equation. Check your solution.

1. $2x + 7 = 3x - 5$

2. $4(x + 2) = 7(x - 1)$

3. $-6 - 2y = 4(3 + y)$

4. $5(2n + 3) = 6n + 23$

5. $\frac{5}{3}b - 11 = \frac{8}{3}b + 4$

6. $-2z = 4(3z - 7)$

7. Find the value of x so that a square with side $x + 1$ has the same perimeter as a triangle with sides $x + 2$, $x + 3$, and $x + 5$.

Name _____

What you should learn:

4.6	How to use tables and graphs to solve problems and how to use a general problem-solving plan

Correlation to Pupil's Textbook:

Chapter Test (p. 191)
Exercises 18–20

Examples	*Using Tables and Graphs and Using a Problem-Solving Plan*

a. In 1969-70, 484,174 men and 343,060 women graduated with bachelor's degrees from U. S. colleges. Over the next twenty years, the number of men graduates both increased and decreased. During the same twenty years, the number of women graduates increased. When was the number of women graduates more than the number of men graduates?

From the table, you can see that the number of women graduates was more than the number of men graduates in 1984-85 and in 1989-90.

Year	Men	Women
1969-70	484,174	343,060
1974-75	533,797	425,052
1979-80	526,327	473,221
1984-85	482,528	496,949
1989-90	491,488	558,169

b. You own a business that produces stadium cushions. Your costs are $2200 plus $6 in materials for each cushion. You sell each cushion for $10. How many cushions must be sold to break even (when your total cost equals your total income)?

Verbal Model

$$\boxed{\text{Total Cost}} = \boxed{\text{Total Income}}$$

$$2200 + 6 \cdot \boxed{\text{Number of cushions}} = 10 \cdot \boxed{\text{Number of cushions}}$$

Labels   Number of cushions $= n$

Algebraic Model

$$2200 + 6n = 10n$$
$$2200 + 6n - 6n = 10n - 6n$$
$$2200 = 4n$$
$$550 = n$$

You must sell 550 cushions to break even.

Guidelines: • When solving real-life problems, you can use a general problem-solving plan:

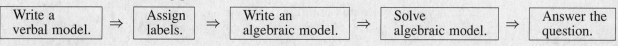

Write a verbal model.	⇒	Assign labels.	⇒	Write an algebraic model.	⇒	Solve algebraic model.	⇒	Answer the question.

EXERCISES

1. Graph the data from Example a above to help you visualize the number of men and women graduates.

2. Use the model from Example b above to find the number of cushions you must sell in order to break even, if you sell the cushions for $14.

Name _____

Examples	*Equations Involving Decimals and Solving Problems with a Table*

a. Solve $3.18(4.32x) = 5.53(4.88)$. Round the solution to 2 decimal places.

$$3.18(4.32x) = 5.53(4.88)$$

$$13.7376x = 26.9864$$

$$\frac{13.7376x}{13.7376} = \frac{26.9864}{13.7376}$$

$$x \approx 1.96$$

The solution is ≈ 1.96. Check this in the original equation.

b. You are mailing a package to your friend. The rates for first class mail are $0.29 for the first ounce and $0.23 for each additional ounce (or fraction of additional ounce). For $1.50, what is the weight to the nearest ounce of the heaviest package you can mail first class? Use a table to solve the problem.

Verbal Model		Total rate	=	Rate of first ounce	+	Rate of additional ounces	·	Number of additional ounces

Labels   Total rate $= R$ (dollars)
                Rate of first ounce $= 0.29$ (dollars)
                Rate of additional ounces $= 0.23$ (dollars)
                Number of additional ounces $= n$ (ounces)

Algebraic $R = 0.29 + 0.23n$
Model

Number of Additional Ounces	1	2	3	4	5	6
Total Rate	0.52	0.75	0.98	1.21	1.44	1.67

From the table, you can see that the heaviest package you can mail first class is 6 ounces (5 additional ounces and the first ounce).

Guidelines: • When solving equations with decimals, your solution is more accurate if you do not round until the final step.

EXERCISES

In Exercises 1–5, use a calculator to solve the equation. Round your result to two decimal places.

1. $45y - 56 = -12$ **2.** $6.5n + 2.4 = 23.7$ **3.** $4.7(9.3x + 2.2) = 59.5$

4. $1.89k + 33.1 = 1.37k - 0.42$ **5.** $3.4(1.6x + 8.9) = 1.2(7.5 - 0.4x)$

6. What is the weight to the nearest ounce of the heaviest package you can mail first class, if you cannot spend more than $3.00?

Reteach
Chapter 4

Name _____

What you should learn:

4.8	How to use formulas from geometry to solve equations and how to use geometry formulas to solve real-life problems

---

Examples *Using Formulas from Geometry and Solving Real-Life Problems*

a. The base of a triangle is four more than twice x. The height is 6. The area is 30 square units. Find the base of the triangle.

$$\text{Area} = \tfrac{1}{2}(\text{base})(\text{height}) \qquad Area\ formula$$

$$30 = \tfrac{1}{2}(2x+4)(6) \qquad \textit{The base of the triangle is } 2x+4.$$

$$30 = (2x+4)3 \qquad \textit{Simplify.}$$

$$10 = 2x+4 \qquad \textit{Divide each side by 3.}$$

$$6 = 2x \qquad \textit{Subtract 4 from each side.}$$

$$3 = x \qquad \textit{Divide each side by 2.}$$

The base is $2(3) + 4 = 10$ units.

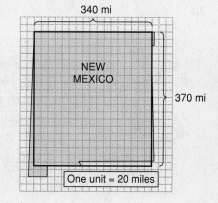

b. Use the map to approximate the area of New Mexico.

The shape of the state of New Mexico is nearly a rectangle. You can use the formula for the area of a rectangle to approximate the area of New Mexico.

$$\text{Area of New Mexico} \approx \text{Area of rectangle}$$
$$= (\text{length})(\text{width})$$
$$= (370)(340)$$
$$= 125{,}800$$

You can estimate the area of New Mexico to be about 126,000 square miles.

Guidelines:

- The formula for the perimeter of a rectangle is $P = 2\,(\text{width}) + 2\,(\text{length})$.

- The formula for the area of a triangle is $A = \tfrac{1}{2}\,(\text{base})(\text{height})$.

- The formula for the area of a rectangle is $A = (\text{length})(\text{width})$.

EXERCISES

In Exercises 1–3, solve for x and find the dimensions of the polygon.

1. Rectangle
   Perimeter: 24 units
   Width: x
   Length: $3x + 4$

2. Triangle
   Area: 63 square units
   Base: 6
   Height: $4x + 1$

3. Square
   Area: 64 square units
   Side: x

4. What is the perimeter of New Mexico?

Name _____

What you should learn:

5.1	How to read and make picture graphs and how to read and make time lines

Correlation to Pupil's Textbook:

Mid-Chapter Self-Test (p. 213)   Chapter Test (p. 237)

Exercise 7   Exercises 1–3

Examples   *Using Picture Graphs and Using Time Lines*

a. The heights of notable U.S. skyscrapers are given below. Use a picture graph to represent this data.

(Source: The 1994 Information Please Almanac)

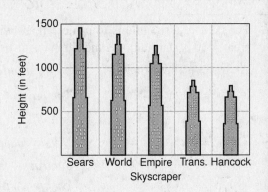

Sears Tower, Chicago	1454 feet
World Trade Center, New York	1377 feet
Empire State Bldg., New York	1250 feet
Transamerica Pyramid, San Francisco	853 feet
John Hancock Tower, Boston	790 feet

One way to represent the heights of notable U.S. skyscrapers is shown at the right.

b. Notable manned and unmanned space flights are listed below. Draw a time line for this data. (Source: Compton's Encyclopedia)

Date	Space Flight
1957	Sputnik 1 - World's first man–made earth satellite
1961	Vostok 1 - World's first manned space flight
1962	Mercury 6 - First U.S. astronaut to orbit earth
1969	Apollo 11 - First men to land on the moon
1973	Skylab - U.S. satellite laboratory
1981	Columbia - First space shuttle

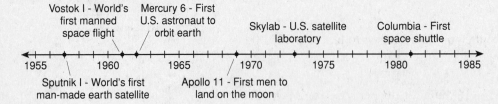

Guidelines:
- A picture graph can be used to compare data.
- A time line is a graph that shows the dates of several occurrences.

EXERCISES

1. In Example a, which two buildings are closest to being the same height?

2. Draw a time line that represents the years in which selected U.S. presidents were inaugurated.

Washington	1789	Lincoln	1861	T. Roosevelt	1901	Kennedy	1961
Jackson	1829	Grant	1869	F. Roosevelt	1933	Clinton	1993

What you should learn:

5.2	How to use bar graphs to represent data and how to use histograms to represent data

Correlation to Pupil's Textbook:

Chapter Test (p. 237)
Exercises 10–13

Examples | *Using Bar Graphs and Using Histograms*

a. The average annual income for year-round full-time workers ages 25 and above is given below for various years. Represent the data with a double bar graph. (Source: Statistical Abstract of the U.S., 1990)

Year	Men	Women	Year	Men	Women
1970	9,521	5,616	1982	22,857	14,477
1974	12,786	7,370	1986	27,335	17,675
1978	16,882	10,121			

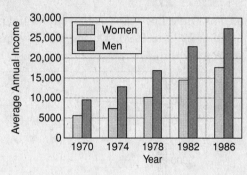

b. You have taken a survey of the weights (in pounds) of each member of your drama club. Organize this data by a histogram.

112, 135, 140, 109, 105, 122, 129, 147, 117, 105, 143, 110, 148, 102

Construct a frequency distribution that shows the number of weights in an interval. Use the numbers in the frequency distribution to draw a histogram.

Frequency Distribution

Interval	Tally	Total
100 - 109	IIII	4
110 - 119	III	3
120 - 129	II	2
130 - 139	I	1
140 - 149	IIII	4

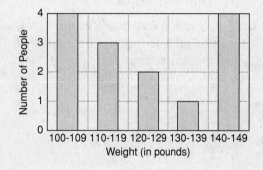

Guidelines:
- The 3 types of bar graphs are simple bar graphs, double (or triple) bar graphs, and stacked bar graphs.
- A histogram is a bar graph in which the bars represent intervals of numbers.

EXERCISES

1. The revenues for the top 5 all-time motion picture money makers are given below. Represent the data with a bar graph.

E.T. The Extra-Terrestrial, $228,618,939; Star Wars, $193,777,000; Return of the Jedi, $169,193,000; Batman, $150,500,000; The Empire Strikes Back, $141,672,000 (Source: Variety, Inc.)

2. For Example b, construct a frequency distribution using these intervals: 101–110, 111–120, 121–130, 131–140, and 141–150.

Reteach
Chapter 5

Name _____

What you should learn:

5.3	How to use line graphs to represent data and how to use line graphs to explore patterns in geometry

Correlation to Pupil's Textbook:

Mid-Chapter Self-Test (p. 213)   **Chapter Test (p. 237)**
Exercises 1–6   Exercises 4, 5

Examples | *Using Line Graphs and Exploring Patterns in Geometry*

a. The triple line graph below shows the numbers of domestic vehicle sales from 1975 to 1990. During which years did every type of vehicle increase in sales? (Source: U.S. Dept. of Commerce, Motorcycle Industry Council, Inc.)

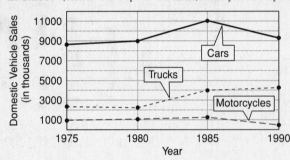

Sales of passenger cars, trucks, and motorcycles increased in 1980–1985.

b. The table shown below lists the width, length, and area of 4 rectangles. Use the table to make a line graph that shows the relationship between the length and the area.

Width	2	2	2	2
Length	2	3	4	5
Area	4	6	8	10

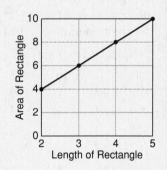

Guidelines:
- Line graphs are often used to show trends over intervals of time.
- Simple, double, and triple line graphs show changes in one, two, and three quantities, respectively.

EXERCISES

In Exercises 1–4 , use the line graph shown at the right.
(Source: Statistical Abstract of the United States:1992)

1. Estimate the public professor salary in 1970 and in 1990.

2. Estimate the private professor salary in 1970 and in 1990.

3. During which time period did the public professor salary increase the least?

4. During which time period did the private professor salary increase the most?

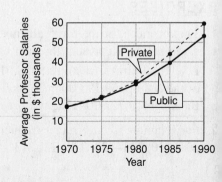

Name _____

What you should learn:

5.4	How to choose an appropriate graph to represent data and how to use graphs to make presentations

Correlation to Pupil's Textbook:

Mid-Chapter Self-Test (p. 213)   Chapter Test (p. 237)
Exercises 8, 9   Exercise 7

Examples | *Choosing Appropriate Graphs and Making Graphical Presentations*

a. Sales for the 5 largest industrial corporations in 1992 are given below. Organize the data graphically. (Source: Fortune)

Corporation	Sales in Billions of Dollars
General Motors	132.8
Exxon	103.5
Ford Motor	100.8
Int'l Business Machines	65.1
General Electric	62.2

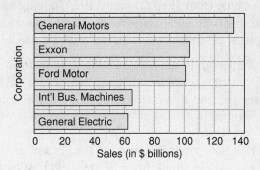

You can use a bar graph because the data falls into more than one category and you want to compare totals.

b. The percent of the civilian labor force that was female is listed below for various years. Organize the data graphically. (Sources: Department of Commerce, Bureau of the Census, and Department of Labor, Bureau of Labor Statistics)

Year	Percent
1910	19.9
1930	22.0
1950	29.6
1970	38.1
1990	45.3

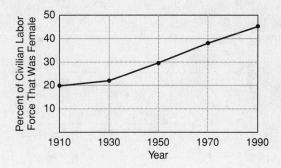

You can use a line graph because you want to show how one category changes over time.

Guidelines:

- When you are using a graph to organize and present data, you must choose an appropriate graph.
- Use a picture graph for informal presentations in which you want a high visual appeal.

EXERCISE

Organize the data with a bar graph. (Source: Natural History Magazine, March, 1974)

Animal	Cheetah	Lion	Zebra	Man	Chicken
Speed (mph)	70	50	40	28	9

Reteach
Chapter 5

What you should learn:

5.5	How to recognize misleading bar graphs and misleading line graphs

Correlation to Pupil's Textbook:

Chapter Test (p. 237)
Exercise 6

Examples | *Misleading Bar Graphs and Misleading Line Graphs*

a. The bar graph at the right shows the U. S. Per Capita Personal Income from 1980 through 1992. Judging only from the length of the bars, compare the 1992 income to the 1980 income.
<small>(Source: Department of Commerce, Bureau of Economic Analysis)</small>

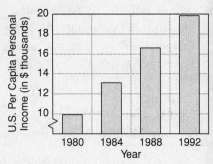

The length of the bars make it seem that the 1992 income is about 6 times the 1980 income. From the scale, you can see that the 1992 income is really only about twice the 1980 income.

b. The line graphs below show the percent of U. S. households heated by natural gas and electricity from 1970 to 1985. Which line graph is misleading? <small>(Source: Bureau of the Census)</small>

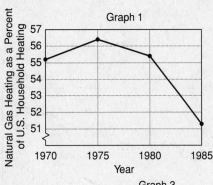

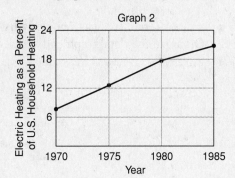

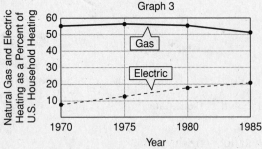

Graph 1 is misleading.

Guidelines:
- Bar graphs can be misleading when vertical scales are broken.
- Line graphs can be misleading when broken vertical scales accentuate the changes from one year to the next.

EXERCISE

Write a paragraph explaining why, in Example b above, Graph 1 is misleading.

Reteach
Chapter 5

Name _____

What you should learn:

5.6	How to use line plots to organize data and how to use organized data to help make decisions

Correlation to Pupil's Textbook:

Chapter Test (p. 237)
Exercises 8, 9

Examples — *Using Line Plots and Using Data in Decision Making*

a. Thirty students in a ninth-grade social studies class were asked to record the number of hours they spent watching television during a specific week. The results are shown below. Organize the data in a line plot.

14, 16, 23, 20, 22, 19, 19, 17, 20, 21, 15, 12, 17, 16, 23,

15, 19, 22, 21, 18, 14, 23, 16, 16, 23, 17, 18, 22, 17, 15

Draw a number line that includes all integers from 12 through 23. For each number in the list, place an X above the coordinate on the line.

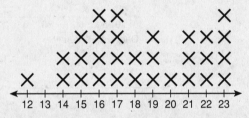

b. You are trying to determine how seriously a group of people view their responsibility to vote. You ask each person in the group to complete a survey question about how often they vote. The results are shown at the right. What would you conclude from the survey question?

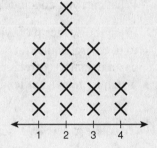

1. I always vote.

2. I usually vote.

3. I usually don't vote.

4. I never vote.

From the survey question, it appears that more than half of the people in the group take their responsibility to vote seriously. Ten of the sixteen people said that they usually or always vote.

Guidelines:

- Deciding how to organize data is a critical part of a branch of mathematics called statistics.
- One way to organize data is with a line plot.

EXERCISE

Twenty students completed a biology test. The scores are shown below. Organize the data in a line plot. What can you conclude from the results?

85, 85, 75, 75, 75, 65, 95, 95, 75, 75, 75, 95, 65, 85, 75, 55, 55, 95, 75, 85

What you should learn:

5.7	How to use scatter plots to organize data and how to use scatter plots to help make decisions

Correlation to Pupil's Textbook:

Chapter Test (p. 237)
Exercises 10, 11

Examples	*Using Scatter Plots and Decision Making with Scatter Plots*

a. As a solution was being heated, 8 temperature readings were taken simultaneously with a Fahrenheit thermometer and a Celsius thermometer. The ordered pairs below show the Fahrenheit temperatures and Celsius temperatures for the 8 measurements. Draw a scatter plot of the data. Does a correlation exist?

(86, 30), (50, 10), (77, 25), (95, 35),
(32, 0), (59, 15), (104, 40), (68, 20)

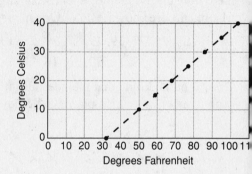

From the scatter plot, you can see that the y-coordinates tend to increase as the x-coordinates increase. This means that the two measurements have a positive correlation.

b. The scatter plot at the right shows students' test scores and the number of hours that students spent watching television each week. What type of correlation does the scatter plot have? What can you conclude?

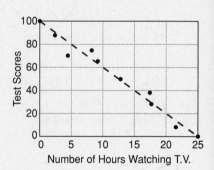

From the scatter plot, you can see that the y-coordinates tend to decrease as the x-coordinates increase. The scatter plot has a negative correlation. So, students who spend more time watching television tend to have lower test scores.

Guidelines:

- A scatter plot is the graph of a collection of ordered pairs of numbers (x, y).

- If no pattern exists between the x and y-coordinates, then x and y have no correlation.

EXERCISES

In Exercises 1–4, decide whether a scatter plot relating the two quantities would tend to have a positive, negative, or no correlation.

1. The arm spread and the height of a person

2. The temperature outside and consumption of hot chocolate

3. A person's weight and test scores

4. The age and value of an antique vase

Name _____

What you should learn:

5.8 How to compute the probability of an event and how to use probability to solve real-life problems

Correlation to Pupil's Textbook:

Chapter Test (p. 237)
Exercise 12

Examples | *Finding the Probability of an Event and Using Probability in Real Life*

a. A wallet contains 1 dime, 3 nickels, 2 quarters, and 4 pennies. If you randomly choose one coin, the probability that it will be a dime is

$$P = \frac{\text{Number of dimes}}{\text{Total number of coins}} = \frac{1}{10} = 0.10.$$

What is the probability that the coin you randomly chose is not a dime?

$$P = \frac{\text{Number of coins that are not dimes}}{\text{Total number of coins}} = \frac{9}{10} = 0.90$$

b. You are taking a poll to find out how often Americans use their automatic-teller machine (ATM) cards. You ask 400 cardholders how many times they use their ATM cards per month. You obtain the following data.

Number of ATM uses per month	0	1	2-3	4-5	6-9	10 or more
Number of cardholders	24	52	88	104	52	80

If you ask another ATM cardholder how often he or she uses the card per month, what is the probability that the response is "4–5 uses"? (Source: Research Partnership)

Of the 400 people sampled, 104 responded "4-5 uses." Assuming that the sample is representative of the entire population, you conclude that the probability is

$$P = \frac{\text{Number of cardholders responding "4-5 uses"}}{\text{Total number of cardholders in survey}} = \frac{104}{400} = \frac{13}{50} = 0.26.$$

The probability that a cardholder will respond "4-5 uses" is $\frac{13}{50}$ or 0.26.

Guidelines:

- The probability of an event is a measure of the likelihood that the event will occur.
- Probability is measured on a scale from 0 to 1.
- Let S be a set that has equally likely outcomes. If E is a subset of S, then the probability that E will occur is

$$\text{Probability of } E = \frac{\text{Number of outcomes in } E}{\text{Number of outcomes in } S}.$$

EXERCISES

In Exercises 1–4, a box contains one red ball, one blue ball, one white ball, and one black ball.

1. What is the probability of picking a red ball?

2. What is the probability of not picking a red ball?

3. What is the probability of picking a red or a blue ball?

4. What is the probability of not picking a red or a blue ball?

Reteach
Chapter 6

Name _____

Correlation to Pupil's Textbook:

Mid-Chapter Self-Test (p. 263)   Chapter Test (p. 287)
Exercises 1–4   Exercises 1, 2

What you should learn:

| 6.1 | How to use divisibility tests and how to factor natural numbers |

Examples   *Using Divisibility Tests and Factoring Natural Numbers*

a. Decide whether 1080 is divisible by 2, 3, 4, 5, 6, 8, 9, and 10.

	Is 1080	
n	divisible by n?	Reason
2	yes	1080 is even.
3	yes	$1 + 0 + 8 + 0 = 9$ and 9 is divisible by 3.
4	yes	80 is divisible by 4.
5	yes	The last digit of 1080 is 0.
6	yes	1080 is even and divisible by 3.
8	yes	80 is divisible by 8.
9	yes	$1 + 0 + 8 + 0 = 9$ and 9 is divisible by 9.
10	yes	The last digit of 1080 is 0.

b. Find all factors of 30.

You can use divisibility tests to factor 30.

Because $\frac{30}{1} = 30$, you conclude that $30 = 1 \cdot 30$.

Because $\frac{30}{2} = 15$, you conclude that $30 = 2 \cdot 15$.

Because $\frac{30}{3} = 10$, you conclude that $30 = 3 \cdot 10$.

Because $\frac{30}{5} = 6$, you conclude that $30 = 5 \cdot 6$.

The factors of 30 are 1, 2, 3, 5, 6, 10, 15, and 30.

Guidelines:
- If one natural number divides evenly into another natural number, then the second number is divisible by the first.
- A natural number is factored when it is written as the product of two or more natural numbers.

EXERCISES

In Exercises 1–8, use the divisibility tests to determine whether the number is divisible by 2, 3, 4, 5, 6, 8, 9, and 10.

1. 615	**2.** 3642	**3.** 985	**4.** 8140
5. 9360	**6.** 5742	**7.** 4320	**8.** 2896

In Exercises 9–16, find all factors of the number.

9. 15	**10.** 48	**11.** 75	**12.** 94
13. 88	**14.** 54	**15.** 70	**16.** 63

Reteach
Chapter 6

Name _____

What you should learn:

6.2	How to classify natural numbers as prime or composite and how to factor algebraic expressions

Correlation to Pupil's Textbook:

Mid-Chapter Self-Test (p. 263)   **Chapter Test (p. 287)**
Exercises 5–7   Exercises 3–6

Examples
Classifying Primes and Composites and Factoring Algebraic Expressions

a. Classify the numbers 19 and 21 as prime or composite.

The natural number 19 is prime because it has exactly two factors, 19 and 1.

The natural number 21 is composite because it has three or more factors.

The factors of 21 are 1, 3, 7, and 21.

b. Write the prime factorization of 105.

Begin by factoring 105 as the product of two numbers other than 1 and itself.

Use a tree diagram to continue factoring until all factors are prime.

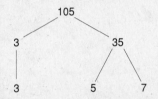

First factor 105 as 3 times 35.

Then factor 35 as 5 times 7.

The prime factorization of 105 is $105 = 3 \cdot 5 \cdot 7$.

c. Write each algebraic expression in expanded form and exponent form.

Expression	Expanded Form	Exponent Form
$12x^2y^3$	$2 \cdot 2 \cdot 3 \cdot x \cdot x \cdot y \cdot y \cdot y$	$2^2 \cdot 3 \cdot x^2 \cdot y^3$
$-40ab^2$	$(-1) \cdot 2 \cdot 2 \cdot 2 \cdot 5 \cdot a \cdot b \cdot b$	$(-1) \cdot 2^3 \cdot 5 \cdot a \cdot b^2$

Guidelines:

- The natural number 1 is neither prime nor composite.
- The expression of a number as the product of all its prime factors is called the prime factorization of the number.

EXERCISES

In Exercises 1–8, write the prime factorization of the number. Write your answer in exponent form.

1. 35   **2.** 98   **3.** 78   **4.** 60

5. 42   **6.** 56   **7.** 54   **8.** 88

In Exercises 9–12, write the expression in expanded form and exponent form.

9. $-16p^2q$ **10.** $-18a^3b^4$ **11.** $20cd^2$ **12.** $70x^2y^4$

In Exercises 13–16, classify the number as prime or composite.

13. 33   **14.** 37   **15.** 47   **16.** 49

Reteach
Chapter 6

Name _____

What you should learn:

6.3	How to find the greatest common factor of two numbers and how to use the greatest common factor to solve real-life problems

Correlation to Pupil's Textbook:

Mid-Chapter Self-Test (p. 263)	Chapter Test (p. 287)
Exercises 8–10	Exercises 7, 8

Examples | *Finding Common Factors and Using Greatest Common Factors*

a. Find the greatest common factor of 32 and 56.

A number that is a factor of both natural numbers 32 and 56 is called a common factor of 32 and 56. Of all common factors of 32 and 56, the largest is called the greatest common factor.

List all the factors of 32 and 56 and select the largest.

The factors of 32 are 1, 2, 4, 8, 16, and 32.

The factors of 56 are 1, 2, 4, 7, 8, 14, 28, and 56.

The common factors are 1, 2, 4, and 8. Of these, 8 is the greatest common factor.

b. Your field hockey team raised $360 for new uniforms and $420 for new equipment. Each team member raised an equal share of the $360 and $420. How much did each team member raise?

Use prime factorization to find the greatest common factor of 360 and 420.

Number	Prime Factorization
360	$2 \cdot 2 \cdot 2 \cdot 3 \cdot 3 \cdot 5$
420	$2 \cdot 2 \cdot 3 \cdot 5 \cdot 7$

From the prime factorization, you conclude that the greatest common factor is $2 \cdot 2 \cdot 3 \cdot 5$ or 60. Each member raised $60.

Guidelines:

- With small numbers, you can find the greatest common factor by listing all factors and selecting the largest.

- With larger numbers, you can find the greatest common factor by writing the prime factorization of each.

EXERCISES

In Exercises 1–8, find the greatest common factor of the numbers or expressions.

1. $18x, 30x^2$

2. $336, 378$

3. $101, 202$

4. $75ab^2, 175a^2b$

5. $686, 980$

6. $235, 245$

7. $90, 135$

8. $40p^2, 84p^3$

What you should learn:

6.4	How to find the least common multiple of two numbers and how to use a least common multiple to solve problems in geometry

Correlation to Pupil's Textbook:

Mid-Chapter Self-Test (p. 263)
Exercises 11–13, 17–20

Chapter Test (p. 287)
Exercises 9–11

Examples | *Finding a Least Common Multiple and Using Least Common Multiples*

a. Find the least common multiple of 14 and 21.

List all the multiples of 14 and 21 and select the smallest.

The multiples of 14 are 14, 28, 42, 56, ...

The multiples of 21 are 21, 42, 63, 84, ...

The smallest duplicate in the two lists, 42, is the least common multiple.

b. Use prime factorization to find the least common multiple of 280 and 300.

Number	Prime Factorization
280	$2 \cdot 2 \cdot 2 \cdot 5 \cdot 7$
300	$2 \cdot 2 \cdot 3 \cdot 5 \cdot 5$

The least common multiple is $2 \cdot 2 \cdot 2 \cdot 3 \cdot 5 \cdot 5 \cdot 7 = 4200$. You should check that 4200 is divisible by 280 and by 300.

c. You are tiling a floor with 14-inch and 10-inch square tiles. Each row contains the same size tile. What is the shortest length you can make the rows if the rows must have the same length?

The least common multiple of 14 and 10 is 70. Each row is 70 inches long.

Guidelines:
- With small numbers, you can find the least common multiple by listing multiples of each number and selecting the smallest.
- With larger numbers, you can find the least common multiple by writing the prime factorization of each.

EXERCISES

In Exercises 1–8, write the prime factorization of each expression. Use the result to find the least common multiple.

1. 20, 25

2. $7x$, $10x^3$

3. 145, 155

4. 18, 22

5. $4a^2b$, $5ab^2$

6. $13p^2$, $26p^3$

7. 120, 200

8. 196, 220

What you should learn:

6.5	How to simplify a fraction and how to compare two fractions

Correlation to Pupil's Textbook:

Mid-Chapter Self-Test (p. 263) **Chapter Test (p. 287)**
Exercises 14-16   Exercises 12, 13

Examples   *Simplifying a Fraction and Comparing Fractions*

a. Simplify the fraction $\dfrac{18x^3}{24x}$.

To simplify a fraction, factor the numerator and denominator. Then divide the numerator and denominator by any common factors.

$$\frac{18x^3}{24x} = \frac{\cancel{2} \cdot 3 \cdot \cancel{3} \cdot \cancel{x} \cdot x \cdot x}{\cancel{2} \cdot 2 \cdot 2 \cdot \cancel{3} \cdot \cancel{x}} = \frac{3x^2}{4}$$

b. Which fraction is larger, $\frac{11}{15}$ or $\frac{13}{20}$?

To compare two fractions, rewrite the fractions with a common denominator. The common denominator should be the least common multiple of the original denominators. The least common multiple of 20 and 15 is 60.

$\frac{11}{15} \cdot \frac{4}{4} = \frac{44}{60}$ *Multiply $\frac{11}{15}$ by $\frac{4}{4}$ to get a denominator of 60.*

$\frac{13}{20} \cdot \frac{3}{3} = \frac{39}{60}$ *Multiply $\frac{13}{20}$ by $\frac{3}{3}$ to get a denominator of 60.*

Because $\frac{44}{60}$ is larger than $\frac{39}{60}$, you can see that $\frac{11}{15}$ is larger than $\frac{13}{20}$.

Another way to compare two fractions is to write them as decimals.

$\frac{11}{15} = 0.7333\ldots$ and $\frac{13}{20} = 0.65$

You can see that $\frac{11}{15}$ is larger than $\frac{13}{20}$.

Guidelines:
- Two fractions are equivalent if they have the same decimal form.
- Writing a fraction in reduced form is called simplifying the fraction.

EXERCISES

In Exercises 1–4, find the greatest common factor of the numerator and denominator. Use your answer to simplify the fraction.

1. $\frac{12}{42}$ 2. $\frac{32}{56}$ 3. $\frac{45}{60}$ 4. $\frac{42}{98}$

In Exercises 5–8, complete the statement with $<$, $>$, or $=$.

5. $\frac{1}{9}$ ☐ $\frac{1}{8}$ 6. $\frac{1}{15}$ ☐ $\frac{1}{16}$ 7. $\frac{6}{7}$ ☐ $\frac{7}{8}$ 8. $\frac{0}{5}$ ☐ $\frac{0}{7}$

Name _____

What you should learn:

6.6	How to show that a number is rational and how to write a decimal as a fraction

Correlation to Pupil's Textbook:

Chapter Test (p. 287)

Exercise 14

Examples | Identifying Rational Numbers and Writing Decimals as Fractions

a. Write the decimal form of the number given and state whether the decimal is terminating, repeating, or nonrepeating. Then decide whether the number is rational or irrational.

Number	Decimal Form	Comment
$\frac{1}{12}$	$0.0833\ldots = 0.08\overline{3}$	Repeating, rational
$\frac{32}{25}$	1.28	Terminating, rational
$\sqrt{3}$	$1.73205080\ldots$	Nonrepeating, irrational
$2\frac{3}{5}$	2.6	Terminating, rational

b. Write the decimal 0.75 as a fraction.

You can write this terminating decimal as a fraction as follows.

$$0.75 = \frac{75}{100} \qquad \textit{Write as 75 hundredths.}$$

$$= \frac{3 \cdot \cancel{5} \cdot \cancel{5}}{2 \cdot 2 \cdot \cancel{5} \cdot \cancel{5}} \qquad \textit{Factor.}$$

$$= \frac{3}{4} \qquad \textit{Simplify.}$$

Guidelines:
- A number is rational if it can be written as the quotient of two integers.
- Numbers that cannot be written as the quotient of two integers are called irrational.

EXERCISES

In Exercises 1–4, follow the directions given in Example a.

1. $\frac{5}{6}$ **2.** $\frac{17}{25}$ **3.** $\sqrt{5}$ **4.** $2\frac{7}{8}$

In Exercises 5–12, write the decimal as a fraction. Simplify the result.

5. 0.46   **6.** 1.4   **7.** 1.72   **8.** 2.3

9. 2.64   **10.** 0.45   **11.** 0.075   **12.** 0.15

Reteach
Chapter 6

What you should learn:

6.7	How to evaluate powers that have negative and zero exponents and how to multiply and divide powers

Correlation to Pupil's Textbook:

Chapter Test (p. 287)

Exercise 15

Examples *Using Negative and Zero Exponents and Multiplying and Dividing Powers*

a. Rewrite each expression without using negative or zero exponents.

$$2^{-3} = \frac{1}{2^3} = \frac{1}{8} \qquad\qquad 17^0 = 1$$

$$(-5)^{-2} = \frac{1}{(-5)^2} = \frac{1}{25} \qquad -5^{-2} = -\frac{1}{5^2} = -\frac{1}{25}$$

b. Simplify each expression, using factors.

$$5^6 \cdot 5^{-2} = 5^6 \cdot \frac{1}{5^2} = \frac{\cancel{5} \cdot \cancel{5} \cdot 5 \cdot 5 \cdot 5 \cdot 5}{\cancel{5} \cdot \cancel{5}} = 5^4$$

$$\frac{6}{6^4} = \frac{\cancel{6}}{\cancel{6} \cdot 6 \cdot 6 \cdot 6} = \frac{1}{6^3}$$

c. Simplify each expression, using exponent rules.

$$3^5 \cdot 3^{-2} = 3^{5+(-2)} = 3^3 \qquad \textit{To multiply two powers with the same}$$
$$\textit{base, add their exponents.}$$

$$\frac{q^3}{q^8} = q^{3-8} = q^{-5} = \frac{1}{q^5} \qquad \textit{To divide two powers with the same}$$
$$\textit{base, subtract the exponent of the}$$
$$\textit{denominator from the exponent of the}$$
$$\textit{numerator.}$$

Guidelines:

- Let n be a positive integer and let a be a nonzero number. The definition of negative and zero exponents is as follows.

$$a^{-n} = \frac{1}{a^n} \text{ and } a^0 = 1$$

- The definition of multiplying and dividing powers is as follows.

$$a^m \cdot a^n = a^{m+n} \text{ and } \frac{a^m}{a^n} = a^{m-n}$$

EXERCISES

In Exercises 1–8, simplify the expression.

1. 12^{-1} **2.** 18^0 **3.** -7^{-2} **4.** $x^4 \cdot x^3$

5. $\dfrac{8^6}{8^2}$ **6.** $\dfrac{t^4}{t^7}$ **7.** $2^0 \cdot 2^5$ **8.** $d^{12} \cdot d^{-7}$

What you should learn:

6.8	How to use scientific notation to represent numbers and how to use scientific notation to solve real life problems

Correlation to Pupil's Textbook:

Chapter Test (p. 287)
Exercises 16–19, 21–23

Examples	*Using Scientific Notation and Using Scientific Notation in Real Life*

a. Write the number in product form, then in scientific notation.

Decimal Form	Product Form	Scientific Notation
78,200	$7.82 \times 10,000$	7.82×10^4

b. Write each number in product form, then in decimal form.

Scientific Notation	Product Form	Decimal Form
4.3×10^{-3}	4.3×0.001	0.0043

c. A light-year, the distance traveled by light in one year, is 5,880,000,000,000 miles. Find the number of miles in 3200 light-years. Write your answer in scientific notation.

Verbal Model

$$\boxed{\text{Total number of miles}} = \boxed{\text{Number of light-years}} \cdot \boxed{\text{Miles in one light-year}}$$

Labels   Number of light-years $= 3200$
              Miles in one light-year $= 5,880,000,000,000$

Algebraic Model

$$\text{Total number of miles} = 3200 \times 5,880,000,000,000$$
$$= (3.2 \times 10^3) \times (5.88 \times 10^{12})$$
$$= (3.2 \times 5.88) \times (10^3 \times 10^{12})$$
$$= 18.816 \times 10^{15}$$
$$= 1.8816 \times 10^{16}$$

The number of miles in 3200 light-years is 1.8816×10^{16}.

Guidelines:

- A number is written in scientific notation if it has the form $c \times 10^n$ where c is greater than or equal to 1 and less than 10.

- To multiply two numbers that are written in scientific notation, you can use the rule for multiplying powers with like bases.

EXERCISES

In Exercises 1–4, write the number in scientific notation.

1. 49890   **2.** 0.12   **3.** 56,600,000   **4.** 0.000089

In Exercises 5–8, write the number in decimal form.

5. 5.67×10^2 **6.** 3.2×10^{-6} **7.** 2.29×10^{-1} **8.** 1.38×10^9

9. The density of a hydrogen atom is 0.00008375 grams per cubic centimeter. Find the density of 1,200 hydrogen atoms. Write your answer in scientific notation and in decimal form.

What you should learn:

6.9	How to recognize number patterns and how to recognize patterns in a coordinate plane

Correlation to Pupil's Textbook:

Chapter Test (p. 287)

Exercise 20

Examples	Recognizing Number Patterns and Patterns in a Coordinate Plane

a. Describe the pattern for the numbers 1, 16, 81, 256, ...
List the next three terms.

The pattern is n^4. The next three terms are 625, 1296, and 2401.

b. Describe the pattern for the numbers 2, 6, 12, 20, ...
List the next three terms.

The pattern is $n(n+1)$. The next three terms are 30, 42, and 56.

c. For each of the following rational numbers $\frac{a}{b}$, plot the
ordered pair (b, a). Then describe the pattern.

$\frac{1}{3}, \frac{3}{5}, \frac{5}{7}, \frac{7}{9}$

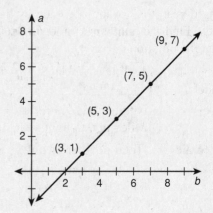

For $\frac{1}{3}$, plot (3, 1).
For $\frac{3}{5}$, plot (5, 3).
For $\frac{5}{7}$, plot (7, 5).
For $\frac{7}{9}$, plot (9, 7).

From the coordinate plane at the right, you can see that all
four points lie on a line.

Guidelines:

- A natural number is called perfect if it is equal to the sum of its factors, except itself.

- A natural number is deficient if it is less than the sum of its factors, except itself.

- A natural number is abundant if it is greater than the sum of its factors, except itself.

EXERCISES

**In Exercises 1–4, show the factors of the number, except itself, and classify
the number as perfect, deficient, or abundant.**

1. 13   **2.** 18   **3.** 19   **4.** 20

In Exercises 5 and 6, describe the pattern. Then list the next three terms.

5. 0, 2, 6, 12, ? ? ?   **6.** 3, 6, 11, 18, ? ? ?

7. For $\frac{7}{1}, \frac{5}{3}, \frac{3}{5}$, and $\frac{1}{7}$, follow the directions in Example c.

Reteach
Chapter 7

What you should learn:

7.1	How to add like fractions and how to subtract like fractions

Correlation to Pupil's Textbook:

Mid-Chapter Self-Test (p. 316) **Chapter Test (p. 341)**
Exercises 1, 2, 10   Exercises 1, 2

Examples | *Adding Like Fractions and Subtracting Like Fractions*

a. To add like fractions, add the numerators and write the sum over the denominator.

$$\frac{-3x}{4} + \frac{5x}{4} = \frac{-3x + 5x}{4} \quad \text{Add numerators.}$$

$$= \frac{2x}{4} \quad \text{Simplify numerator.}$$

$$= \frac{2x}{2 \cdot 2} \quad \text{Factor denominator.}$$

$$= \frac{x}{2} \quad \text{Simplify fraction.}$$

b. You can use the rules for adding and subtracting like fractions to solve equations with like fractions.

$$x + \frac{1}{8} = \frac{5}{8}$$

$$x + \frac{1}{8} - \frac{1}{8} = \frac{5}{8} - \frac{1}{8} \quad \text{Subtract } \tfrac{1}{8} \text{ to each side.}$$

$$x = \frac{4}{8} \quad \text{Subtract numerators.}$$

$$x = \frac{2 \cdot 2}{2 \cdot 2 \cdot 2} \quad \text{Factor numerator and denominator.}$$

$$x = \frac{1}{2} \quad \text{Simplify fraction.}$$

Guidelines: • Like fractions are fractions that have the same denominator.

EXERCISES

In Exercises 1–8, add or subtract. Then simplify, if possible.

1. $\frac{1}{7} + \frac{5}{7}$

2. $-\frac{5}{13} + -\frac{4}{13}$

3. $3\frac{1}{5} - 1\frac{2}{5}$

4. $\frac{6}{10} - \frac{2}{10}$

5. $\frac{x}{3} + \frac{4x}{3}$

6. $\frac{-2a}{9} - \frac{a}{9}$

7. $\frac{1}{4y} + \frac{2}{4y}$

8. $\frac{5b}{6} - \frac{7b}{6}$

In Exercises 9–12, solve the equation. Then simplify, if possible.

9. $x - \frac{1}{3} = \frac{7}{3}$

10. $n + \frac{3}{6} = \frac{4}{6}$

11. $s + \frac{12}{9} = -\frac{4}{9}$

12. $z - \frac{5}{8} = -\frac{3}{8}$

Name _____

What you should learn:

| 7.2 | How to add and subtract unlike fractions and how to use addition and subtraction of fractions to solve real-life problems |

Correlation to Pupil's Textbook:

Mid-Chapter Self-Test (p. 316)   **Chapter Test (p. 341)**
Exercises 3, 4, 9, 13   Exercises 3, 4

| Example | *Adding and Subtracting Unlike Fractions and Solving Real-Life Problems* |

a. The prime interest rate went up $\frac{3}{4}$ of a percentage point in May, went up another $\frac{1}{2}$ of a percentage point in June, and fell $\frac{3}{8}$ of a percentage point in July. What is the total change in the prime interest rate for these three months?

Verbal Model

$$\boxed{\text{Total change}} = \boxed{\text{May change}} + \boxed{\text{June change}} + \boxed{\text{July change}}$$

Labels

Total change $= T$ (percentage point)
May change $= \frac{3}{4}$ (percentage point)
June change $= \frac{1}{2}$ (percentage point)
July change $= -\frac{3}{8}$ (percentage point)

Algebraic Model

$$T = \frac{3}{4} + \frac{1}{2} + \left(-\frac{3}{8}\right)$$

$$= \frac{3}{4} \cdot \frac{2}{2} + \frac{1}{2} \cdot \frac{4}{4} + \left(-\frac{3}{8}\right) \qquad \text{\textit{Least common denominator is 8.}}$$

$$= \frac{6}{8} + \frac{4}{8} + \left(-\frac{3}{8}\right) \qquad \text{\textit{Rewrite as like fractions.}}$$

$$= \frac{6 + 4 + (-3)}{8} \qquad \text{\textit{Add the like fractions.}}$$

$$= \frac{7}{8} \qquad \text{\textit{Simplify.}}$$

The total increase in the prime interest rate was $\frac{7}{8}$ of a percentage point.

Guidelines: • The least common denominator of two fractions is the least common multiple of their denominators.

EXERCISES

In Exercises 1–8, find the sum or difference. Then simplify, if possible.

1. $\frac{1}{5} - \frac{3}{10}$

2. $\frac{2}{9} + \frac{3}{4}$

3. $-\frac{1}{3} + -\frac{5}{6}$

4. $-\frac{3}{8} - \frac{1}{4}$

5. $\frac{a}{7} + \frac{3a}{14}$

6. $\frac{x}{2} - \frac{3x}{7}$

7. $\frac{4}{p} + \frac{5}{q}$

8. $\frac{1}{2} - \frac{11}{y}$

9. Refer to Example a. If the prime interest rate continued to fall $\frac{5}{8}$ of a percentage point in August, and then went up $\frac{1}{4}$ of a percentage point in September, what is the total change for the five-month period?

Name _____

What you should learn:

| 7.3 | How to add and subtract fractions by writing the fractions as decimals and how to use addition and subtraction of decimals to solve real-life problems |

Correlation to Pupil's Textbook:
Mid-Chapter Self-Test (p. 316)
Exercise 19

Examples | *Adding and Subtracting Decimals and Solving Real-Life Problems*

a. Evaluate the expression by first rewriting in decimal form. Round the numbers to 3 decimal places, then round the result to 2 decimal places.

$$\frac{5y}{9} - \frac{3y}{8} \approx 0.556y - 0.375y \qquad \textit{Write as rounded decimals.}$$

$$= 0.181y \qquad \textit{Subtract decimals.}$$

$$\approx 0.18y \qquad \textit{Round to 2 decimal places.}$$

b. The circle graph at the right shows the results of a survey of students' favorite high school subjects. What portion of the students named English as their favorite subject?

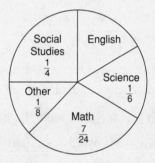

The fractions for the five parts have a sum of 1. To find the portion of the students that named English as their favorite subject, add the other four fractions and subtract the result from 1. Round the numbers to 3 decimal places, then round the result to 2 decimal places.

$$x = 1 - \left(\tfrac{1}{6} + \tfrac{7}{24} + \tfrac{1}{8} + \tfrac{1}{4}\right)$$

$$\approx 1 - (0.167 + 0.292 + 0.125 + 0.25)$$

$$= 1 - 0.834$$

$$\approx 0.17$$

This means that about 17 out of every 100 students named English as their favorite subject.

Guidelines:

- When you add or subtract fractions by first rewriting the fractions as decimals, remember that the result may be only approximate.

- To avoid a round-off error, you should begin by rounding the numbers to one place more than is required in the final result.

EXERCISES

In Exercises 1–6, use a calculator to evaluate the expression by first rewriting in decimal form. Round your result to two decimal places.

1. $\dfrac{9}{16} + \dfrac{2}{7}$

2. $\dfrac{4}{22} - \dfrac{17}{19}$

3. $\dfrac{2x}{15} + \dfrac{5x}{29}$

4. $1 - \left(\dfrac{2}{9} + \dfrac{3}{11}\right)$

5. $2\dfrac{1}{10} + 4\dfrac{1}{8} - 1\dfrac{3}{4}$

6. $\dfrac{4n}{13} - \dfrac{2n}{39} + \dfrac{3n}{17}$

Name _____

What you should learn:

7.4	How to multiply rational numbers and how to use multiplication of rational numbers to solve real-life problems

Correlation to Pupil's Textbook:

Mid-Chapter Self-Test (p. 316)   **Chapter Test (p. 341)**

Exercises 5, 6, 11, 13–15,   Exercises 5, 7
17, 18, 20

Examples	*Multiplying Rational Numbers and Solving Real-Life Problems*

a. To multiply rational numbers, multiply the numerators and multiply the denominators.

$$\frac{3}{4} \cdot \frac{5y}{12} = \frac{3 \cdot 5y}{4 \cdot 12} \qquad \text{\textit{Multiply numerators and denominators.}}$$

$$= \frac{15y}{48} \qquad \text{\textit{Simplify numerator and denominator.}}$$

$$= \frac{\cancel{3} \cdot 5 \cdot y}{\cancel{3} \cdot 16} \qquad \text{\textit{Factor numerator and denominator.}}$$

$$= \frac{5y}{16} \qquad \text{\textit{Simplify fraction.}}$$

b. Find the area of the rectangle shown at the right, with a width of $2\frac{2}{3}$ centimeters and a length of $4\frac{3}{4}$ centimeters.

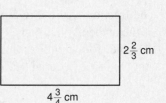

$2\frac{2}{3}$ cm

$4\frac{3}{4}$ cm

To find the area, multiply the width by the length.

$$\text{Area} = (\text{Width}) \times (\text{Length})$$

$$= 2\frac{2}{3} \times 4\frac{3}{4}$$

$$= \frac{8}{3} \times \frac{19}{4}$$

$$= \frac{8 \cdot 19}{3 \cdot 4}$$

$$= \frac{\cancel{4} \cdot 2 \cdot 19}{3 \cdot \cancel{4}} = \frac{38}{3} \text{ square centimeters}$$

The area of the rectangle is about 12.7 square centimeters.

Guidelines: • The rule for multiplying fractions applies whether the denominators are like or unlike.

EXERCISES

In Exercises 1–8, multiply. Then simplify, if possible.

1. $\frac{3}{5} \cdot \frac{4}{7}$ **2.** $-\frac{2}{3} \cdot \frac{6}{11}$ **3.** $3\frac{1}{4} \cdot 2\frac{5}{6}$ **4.** $-1\frac{4}{9} \cdot \left(-4\frac{1}{3}\right)$

5. $\frac{-9x}{13} \cdot \frac{5}{3}$ **6.** $\frac{18a}{7} \cdot \frac{5}{6a}$ **7.** $\frac{-17t}{20} \cdot \frac{-2}{t^2}$ **8.** $-\frac{4}{15} \cdot \frac{5}{9} \cdot \frac{-6}{8}$

Name _____

| Examples | *Dividing Rational Numbers and Solving Real-Life Problems* |

a. Simplify the expression.

$$\frac{3x}{4} \div 6 = \frac{3x}{4} \cdot \frac{1}{6} \qquad \text{\textit{Reciprocal of 6 is } } \tfrac{1}{6}.$$

$$= \frac{3x}{24} \qquad \text{\textit{Multiply fractions.}}$$

$$= \frac{3x}{3 \cdot 8} \qquad \text{\textit{Factor denominator.}}$$

$$= \frac{x}{8} \qquad \text{\textit{Simplify fraction.}}$$

b. Your neighbor paid you $14.00 for cutting his grass. You worked for $3\frac{1}{2}$ hours. What was your hourly wage?

To find your hourly wage, divide the money you earned by the hours that you worked.

$$14 \text{ dollars} \div 3\tfrac{1}{2} \text{ hours} = 14 \text{ dollars} \div \frac{7 \text{ hours}}{2}$$

$$= 14 \text{ dollars} \cdot \frac{2}{7 \text{ hours}}$$

$$= \frac{28 \text{ dollars}}{7 \text{ hours}}$$

$$= \frac{4 \text{ dollars}}{\text{hour}}$$

Your hourly wage was $4.00 per hour.

Guidelines:

- To divide by a fraction, multiply by its reciprocal.
- Negative fractions can be written as follows:

$$-\frac{a}{b} \quad \text{or} \quad \frac{-a}{b} \quad \text{or} \quad \frac{a}{-b}$$

EXERCISES

In Exercises 1–8, simplify the expression.

1. $\frac{6}{7} \div -3$

2. $-\frac{2}{3} \div \frac{4}{3}$

3. $5\frac{1}{2} \div \frac{1}{2}$

4. $-\frac{9}{10} \div -\frac{6}{5}$

5. $1\frac{3}{5} \div \frac{8}{x}$

6. $y \div -2\frac{1}{4}$

7. $14 \div \frac{1}{7z}$

8. $\frac{18a}{5} \div \frac{9a}{2}$

Reteach
Chapter 7

Name _____

What you should learn:

7.6	How to write portions as percents and how to use percents to solve real-life problems

Correlation to Pupil's Textbook:

Chapter Test (p. 341)
Exercises 15, 17, 18

Examples — *Writing Percents and Solving Real-Life Problems*

a. A percent is a portion whose denominator is 100. The symbol % means percent. Complete the table for each of the following portions.

Portion	Fraction Form	Percent Symbol Form	Verbal Form
$\frac{22}{40}$	$\frac{22}{40} = \frac{11}{20} = \frac{55}{100}$	55%	55 percent
$\frac{6}{15}$	$\frac{6}{15} = \frac{2}{5} = \frac{40}{100}$	40%	40 percent

b. Which of the following has a lesser percent of its area shaded?

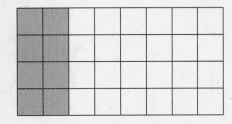   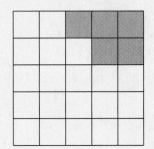

The portion of the region that is shaded is

$$\frac{8}{32} = \frac{1}{4} = \frac{1 \cdot 25}{4 \cdot 25} = \frac{25}{100} = 25\%.$$

The portion of the region that is shaded is

$$\frac{5}{25} = \frac{1}{5} = \frac{1 \cdot 20}{5 \cdot 20} = \frac{20}{100} = 20\%.$$

The figure at the right has a lesser percent of its area shaded.

Guidelines:

- A portion is a fraction that compares the measure of part of a quantity to the measure of the whole quantity.
- When the denominator is 100, the portion is called a percent.

EXERCISES

In Exercises 1–8, write each portion as a percent.

1. $\frac{1}{5}$ 2. $\frac{7}{20}$ 3. $\frac{8}{25}$ 4. $\frac{12}{15}$

5. $\frac{22}{44}$ 6. $\frac{14}{56}$ 7. $\frac{25}{250}$ 8. $\frac{120}{160}$

Reteach
Chapter 7

Name _____

What you should learn:

7.7	How to write percents as decimals and how to write decimals and fractions as percents

Correlation to Pupil's Textbook:

Chapter Test (p. 341)
Exercises 9–12, 14

Examples *Writing Percents as Decimals and Writing Decimals and Fractions as Percents*

a. Rewrite 1.7% as a decimal.

$$1.7\% = \frac{1.7}{100}$$

$$= 0.017$$

To write a percent as a decimal, remove the percent sign and divide by 100.

b. Rewrite 2.4 as a percent.

$$2.4 = 2.4(100\%)$$

$$= 240\%$$

To write a decimal as a percent, multiply the decimal by 100%.

c. Rewrite $\frac{9}{8}$ as a percent.

$$\frac{9}{8} = 1.125$$

$$= 1.125(100\%)$$

$$= 112.5\%$$

To rewrite a fraction as a percent, first rewrite the fraction in decimal form. Then multiply by 100%.

Guidelines:

- When you are rewriting a percent in decimal form, remember that percent means per hundred.
- Some percents are greater than 100% and some percents are less than 1%.

EXERCISES

In Exercises 1–4, rewrite the percent as a decimal.

1. 58% **2.** 120% **3.** $2\frac{3}{10}\%$ **4.** 63.4%

In Exercises 5–8, rewrite the decimal as a percent.

5. 0.4 **6.** 0.033 **7.** 3.24 **8.** 0.002

In Exercises 9–12, rewrite the fraction as a percent.

9. $\frac{14}{112}$ **10.** $\frac{81}{135}$ **11.** $\frac{45}{12}$ **12.** $\frac{203}{116}$

What you should learn:

7.8	How to find a percent of a number and how to use percents to solve real-life problems

Correlation to Pupil's Textbook:

Chapter Test (p. 341)
Exercises 13, 16–18

| **Examples** | *Finding a Percent of a Number and Solving Real-Life Problems* |

a. Find 80% of 130.

Begin by writing 80% as 0.80. Then multiply by 130.

$$0.80 \times 130 = 104$$

Thus, 80% of 130 is 104.

b. Find 115% of 60.

Begin by writing 115% as 1.15. Then multiply by 60.

$$1.15 \times 60 = 69$$

Thus, 115% of 60 is 69.

c. You are buying a compact disc that has a discount of 40%. The original price of the disc is $15. How much is the discount?

To find the discount rate, rewrite 40% as 0.40 and multiply by the original price.

$$0.40 \times 15 = 6$$

The amount of the discount is $6.00.

Guidelines:
- One way to find a percent of a number is to multiply the decimal form of the percent by the number.

EXERCISES

In Exercises 1–4, write the percent as a decimal. Then multiply to find the percent of the number.

1. 15% of 120   **2.** 7% of 500   **3.** 125% of 16   **4.** 240% of 80

In Exercises 5–8, match the percent phrase with the fraction phrase. Then find the percent of the number.

a. $\frac{3}{4}$ of 180   b. $\frac{1}{2}$ of 180   c. $\frac{2}{3}$ of 180   d. $\frac{1}{8}$ of 180

5. 12.5% of 180   **6.** 50% of 180   **7.** 75% of 180   **8.** $66\frac{2}{3}$% of 180

9. You are buying a video cassette that has a discount of 30%. The original price of the video cassette is $20. How much is the discount?

Name _____

What you should learn:

7.9	How to use percents to solve real-life problems and how to use percents to help organize data

Correlation to Pupil's Textbook:

Chapter Test (p. 341)
Exercises 19, 20

Examples — *Using Percents in Real Life and Using Percents to Organize Data*

a. The federal individual income tax rates for single taxpayers are as follows.

Federal Income Tax Brackets - 1993

Taxable Income	Tax Rate
$0 - 22,100	15%
$22,100 - 53,500	28%
$53,500 - 115,000	31%
$115,000 - 250,000	36%
$250,000 and up	39.6%

How much income tax must be paid on a taxable income of $54,000?

The tax rate on taxable income of $54,000 is 31%.

$$31\% \times 54,000 = 0.31 \times 54,000 = 16,740$$

Thus, income tax of $16,740 must be paid on a taxable income of $54,000.

b. In 1993, a research organization surveyed 93,100,000 households with television sets. Show how you could use percents to organize the results.

(Source: Nielson Media Research, May 1993)

Type of TV Set	Number of Homes
Color TV sets	91,238,000
B & W	1,862,000
Cable	57,200,340

You can calculate percents and organize the results with a bar graph.

$$\frac{91,238,000}{93,100,000} = 98\%$$

$$\frac{1,862,000}{93,100,000} = 2\%$$

$$\frac{57,200,340}{93,100,000} \approx 61\%$$

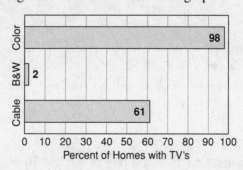

Percent of Homes with TV's

Guidelines:

• To find the amount of a state sales tax on a purchase, change the sales tax percent to a decimal and multiply by the amount of the purchase.

EXERCISES

1. Use the income tax rates in Example a above. How much income tax must be paid on a taxable income of $218,000?

2. Using the bar graph in Example b, what conclusions can you draw about homes with TV's?

Reteach
Chapter 8

Name _____

What you should learn:

Correlation to Pupil's Textbook:

Mid-Chapter Self-Test (p. 362)   Chapter Test (p. 387)

Exercises 1–4   Exercises 1, 4, 7

8.1   How to find rates and how to find ratios

| **Examples** | *Finding Rates and Finding Ratios* |

a. You ran a 10-kilometer race in 40 minutes. What was your average speed, in kilometers per hour?

To find the rate, divide the distance by the time. To find the rate in kilometers per hour, change 40 minutes to $\frac{2}{3}$ hours.

$$\boxed{\text{Rate}} = \frac{\boxed{\text{Distance}}}{\boxed{\text{Time}}} \qquad \textit{Verbal model}$$

$$= \frac{10 \text{ kilometers}}{\frac{2}{3} \text{ hours}} \qquad \textit{Substitute for distance and time.}$$

$$= 10 \times \frac{3}{2} \qquad \textit{Multiply by the reciprocal of } \frac{2}{3}.$$

$$= 15 \text{ kilometers per hour} \qquad \textit{Simplify.}$$

Your rate (or average speed) was 15 kilometers per hour.

b. Write the quotient $\dfrac{2 \text{ hours}}{400 \text{ minutes}}$ as a ratio, then simplify.

To find a ratio, both quantities must have the same unit of measure.

$$\frac{2 \text{ hours}}{400 \text{ minutes}} = \frac{2(60 \text{ minutes})}{400 \text{ minutes}} = \frac{120 \text{ minutes}}{400 \text{ minutes}} = \frac{3}{10} \text{ or 3 to 10.}$$

Guidelines:

- If two quantities a and b have different units of measure, then the rate of a per b is a/b.
- If two quantities a and b have the same units of measure, then the ratio of a to b is a/b.

EXERCISES

In Exercises 1–3, determine whether the quotient is a rate or a ratio. Then simplify.

1. $\dfrac{16 \text{ miles}}{30 \text{ miles}}$ 2. $\dfrac{99 \text{ yards}}{18 \text{ carries}}$ 3. $\dfrac{375 \text{ revolutions}}{5 \text{ minutes}}$

In Exercises 4–6, write each quotient as a ratio and simplify.

4. $\dfrac{220 \text{ meters}}{4 \text{ kilometers}}$ 5. $\dfrac{3 \text{ yards}}{12 \text{ feet}}$ 6. $\dfrac{2 \text{ miles}}{2640 \text{ yards}}$ (1 mi = 1760 yd)

7. The record for rainfall in a 24-hour period is 43 inches at Alvin, Texas on July 25-26, 1979. At what rate did the rain fall on that day?

8. You work for 8 hours and get paid $36. What is your rate of pay?

Name _____

What you should learn:

8.2	How to solve proportions and how to write proportions

Correlation to Pupil's Textbook:

Mid-Chapter Self-Test (p. 362) Chapter Test (p. 387)
Exercises 5–9, 13–16, 19, 20   Exercises 2, 3, 14–16

Examples | *Solving Proportions and Writing Proportions*

a. Use the Reciprocal Property to solve the proportion for z: $\dfrac{5}{4} = \dfrac{9}{z}$.

$$\frac{5}{4} = \frac{9}{z} \qquad \textit{Rewrite original proportion.}$$

$$\frac{5}{4} = \frac{z}{9} \qquad \textit{Reciprocal Property: If } \frac{a}{b} = \frac{c}{d}, \textit{ then } \frac{b}{a} = \frac{d}{c}.$$

$$9 \cdot \frac{4}{5} = \frac{z}{9} \cdot 9 \qquad \textit{Multiply each side by } 9.$$

$$\frac{36}{5} = z \qquad \textit{Simplify.}$$

The solution is $\frac{36}{5}$. Check this in the original proportion.

b. The triangles at the right are similar. Find f.

If two triangles are similar, then the ratios of corresponding sides are equal. Write and solve a proportion that involves f.

$$\frac{f}{c} = \frac{e}{b} \qquad \textit{Ratios of corresponding sides are equal.}$$

$$\frac{f}{13} = \frac{24}{12} \qquad \textit{Substitute for } b, c, \textit{ and } e.$$

$$13 \cdot \frac{f}{13} = 13 \cdot \frac{24}{12} \qquad \textit{Multiply each side by } 13.$$

$$f = 26 \qquad \textit{Simplify.}$$

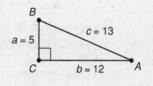

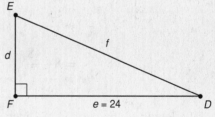

Guidelines:
- An equation that equates two ratios is a proportion.
- You can solve or check a proportion by using the Cross Product Property, which states that if $\frac{a}{b} = \frac{c}{d}$, then $ad = bc$.

EXERCISES

In Exercises 1–3, solve the proportion. Check your solution.

1. $\dfrac{a}{28} = \dfrac{3}{7}$ **2.** $\dfrac{20}{y} = \dfrac{2}{4}$ **3.** $\dfrac{7}{12} = \dfrac{r}{2}$

In Exercises 4–6, write the sentence as a proportion. Then solve.

4. 3 is to 4 as 9 is to x.   **5.** x is to 10 as 5 is to 4.   **6.** 1 is to 8 as y is to 4.

7. Refer to the triangles above to find d.

Reteach
Chapter 8

What you should learn:

8.3	How to use proportions to solve real-life problems

Correlation to Pupil's Textbook:

Mid-Chapter Self-Test (p. 362)
Exercise 17

Chapter Test (p. 387)
Exercises 14–16

Example	*Solving Real-Life Problems*

a. An architect draws plans for a wooden deck, using a scale of $\frac{1}{4}$ inch = 1 foot. The length of the deck in the plans is 8 inches. What is the actual length of the deck?

The ratio of the plans deck length to the actual deck length is

$$\frac{\frac{1}{4} \text{ inch}}{1 \text{ foot}} = \frac{\frac{1}{4} \text{ inch}}{12 \text{ inches}} \qquad \textit{Rewrite 1 foot as 12 inches.}$$

$$= \frac{1}{4} \cdot \frac{1}{12} \qquad \textit{Multiply by the reciprocal of 12.}$$

$$= \frac{1}{48} \qquad \textit{Simplify.}$$

Verbal Model
$$\frac{\boxed{\text{Plans deck length}}}{\boxed{\text{Actual deck length}}} = \frac{\boxed{1}}{\boxed{48}}$$

Labels
Plans deck length $= 8$ (inches)
Actual deck length $= x$ (inches)

Algebraic Model
$$\frac{8}{x} = \frac{1}{48} \qquad \textit{Proportion}$$

$$\frac{x}{8} = \frac{48}{1} \qquad \textit{Reciprocal Property}$$

$$8 \cdot \frac{x}{8} = 8 \cdot \frac{48}{1} \qquad \textit{Multiply each side by 8.}$$

$$x = 384 \qquad \textit{Simplify.}$$

The length of the deck is 384 inches. To convert this measurement to feet, divide by 12 to obtain a length of 32 feet.

Guidelines:
- To solve problems involving scales, rewrite the scale as a proportion.

EXERCISE

1. You are building a scale model of a motorcycle. The model is constructed on a scale of 1 inch $= 28$ inches. The diameter of the wheel on the model is $1\frac{1}{4}$ inches. What is the diameter of the wheel on the actual motorcycle?

What you should learn:

8.4	How to find what percent one number is of another and how to solve a percent equation

Correlation to Pupil's Textbook:

Mid-Chapter Self-Test (p. 362)   **Chapter Test (p. 387)**
Exercises 10–12, 18   Exercises 8, 9

Examples | *Finding Percents and Solving Percent Equations*

a. You scored 19 points on a 25-point history paper. Find the percent p that you scored on the paper.

The statement "a is what percent of b" is equivalent to the percent equation $\dfrac{a}{b} = \dfrac{p}{100}$.

$\dfrac{19}{25} = \dfrac{p}{100}$ *Write percent equation.*

$0.76 = \dfrac{p}{100}$ *Divide to obtain decimal form.*

$76 = p$ *Multiply each side by 100.*

You scored 76% on the paper.

b. You buy a shirt that is discounted $12. The discount is 30% of the original price. What is the original price?

Given a and p, solve for b in the percent equation.

$\dfrac{12}{b} = \dfrac{30}{100}$ *Write in fraction form.*

$\dfrac{b}{12} = \dfrac{100}{30}$ *Write reciprocal of each side.*

$b = \dfrac{100}{30} \cdot 12$ *Multiply each side by 12.*

$b = 40$ *Simplify.*

The original price is $40.

Guidelines:

- In the percent equation, b is the base and a is the number that is compared to the base.

- The third type of percent problem, What is p percent of b?, can be solved by substituting p and b into the percent equation and solving for a.

EXERCISES

In Exercises 1–6, solve the percent equation. Round your answer to 2 decimal places.

1. What is 24 percent of 210?

2. 18 is 75% of what number?

3. 66 is what percent of 150?

4. 115 is what percent of 30?

5. What is 86.4% of 452?

6. 70 is 250 percent of what number?

Reteach
Chapter 8

What you should learn:

8.5	How to use percents to solve real-life problems and how to use percents to find discounts

Correlation to Pupil's Textbook:

Chapter Test (p. 387)
Exercises 10, 11

Examples *Solving Real-Life Problems and Finding Discounts*

a. The students in an English class conducted a survey of the average number of hours per week that the students watch television. The results are shown in the circle graph at the right. Twenty-five students were surveyed. How many responded "20 hours or more"?

Verbal
Model

$$\frac{\boxed{\text{Number responding "20 hours or more"}}}{\boxed{\text{Number surveyed}}} = \frac{\boxed{\text{Percent}}}{\boxed{100}}$$

Labels   Number responding "20 hours or more" $= a$ (students)
          Number surveyed $= 25$ (students)
          Percent $= 40$ (percent)

Algebraic $\dfrac{a}{25} = \dfrac{40}{100}$ *Percent equation*
Model

$25 \cdot \dfrac{a}{25} = 25 \cdot \dfrac{40}{100}$ *Multiply each side by 25.*

$a = 10$ *Simplify.*

Ten students responded "20 hours or more."

b. A $25 sweatshirt is on sale for $18. Find the discount and find the discount percent.

To find the discount, subtract the sale price from the original price.

$25 - 18 = \$7$ *Discount*

To find the discount percent, divide the discount by the regular price.

$$\frac{\boxed{\text{Discount}}}{\boxed{\text{Regular Price}}} = \frac{7}{25}$$ *Divide discount by regular price.*

$= 0.28$ *Rewrite in decimal form.*

$= 28\%$ *Rewrite in percent form.*

Guidelines:
- The discount is the difference between the regular price and the sale price.
- To find the discount percent, use the regular price as the base.

EXERCISES

1. Use the circle graph above to find how many students responded "less than 15 hours" and how many responded " 15-20 hours."

2. A $45 pair of jeans are on sale for $35.10. Find the discount and find the discount percent.

What you should learn:

8.6	How to find a percent of increase and how to find a percent of decrease

Correlation to Pupil's Textbook:

Chapter Test (p. 387)
Exercises 5, 6

Examples | *Finding a Percent of Increase and Finding a Percent of Decrease*

a. In 1990, the enrollment in U.S. public colleges was 10,754,000 students. In 1992, the enrollment was 11,065,000 students. Find the percent of increase from 1990 to 1992. (Source: Department of Commerce, Bureau of the Census)

The percent of change of a quantity is given by $\dfrac{\text{Actual change}}{\text{Original amount}}$.

To find the percent of increase, find the ratio of 311,000 (the increase) to 10,754,000.

$$\dfrac{\boxed{\begin{array}{c}\text{Enrollment}\\\text{in 1992}\end{array}} - \boxed{\begin{array}{c}\text{Enrollment}\\\text{in 1990}\end{array}}}{\boxed{\begin{array}{c}\text{Enrollment}\\\text{in 1990}\end{array}}} = \dfrac{311,000}{10,754,000}$$

$$\approx 0.029 = 2.9\%$$

The percent of increase is about 2.9%.

b. In 1980, the population of West Virginia was 1,949,644. In 1990, the population was 1,793,477. Find the percent of decrease from 1980 to 1990. (Source: Department of Commerce, Bureau of the Census)

To find the percent of decrease, find the ratio of 156,167 (the decrease) to 1,949,644.

$$\dfrac{\boxed{\begin{array}{c}\text{Population}\\\text{in 1980}\end{array}} - \boxed{\begin{array}{c}\text{Population}\\\text{in 1990}\end{array}}}{\boxed{\begin{array}{c}\text{Population}\\\text{in 1980}\end{array}}} = \dfrac{156,167}{1,949,644}$$

$$\approx 0.08 = 8\%$$

The percent of decrease is about 8%.

Guidelines:

- A percent of increase or percent of decrease compares how much a quantity has changed.
- This percent is a percent of increase if the quantity increased and it is a percent of decrease if the quantity decreased.

EXERCISES

In Exercises 1 and 2, decide whether the change is an increase or a decrease and find the percent.

1. 1991: $320.25
1993: $433.50

2. Opening Balance: $3422
Closing Balance: $3267

What you should learn:

8.7	How to use the Counting Principle and how to use Pascal's Triangle to count the number of ways an event can happen

Correlation to Pupil's Textbook:

Chapter Test (p. 387)
Exercises 17, 18

Examples | *Using the Counting Principle and Using Pascal's Triangle*

a. Your high school needs two new teachers, one in English and one in Social Studies. In how many ways can these positions be filled if there are four applicants for the English position and three applicants for the Social Studies position? Confirm your answer by showing a tree diagram.

Use the Counting Principle which states: If one event can occur in 4 ways and another event can occur in 3 ways, then the two events can occur in $4 \cdot 3$ or 12 ways.

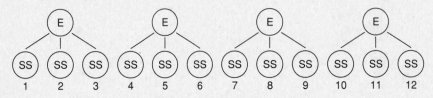

b. You are ordering pizza with 2 toppings. The 4 choices of toppings are cheese, mushroom, sausage, or pepperoni. Use Pascal's Triangle to find the number of ways that you can order the pizza. Confirm your answer by listing the different kinds of pizza.

You can use the 4th row of Pascal's Triangle to find the number of ways you can choose 2 toppings from a group of 4 toppings.

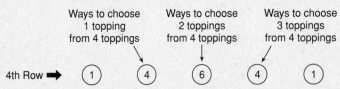

Ways to choose 1 topping from 4 toppings → (4)
Ways to choose 2 toppings from 4 toppings → (6)
Ways to choose 3 toppings from 4 toppings → (4)

4th Row ➡ (1) (4) (6) (4) (1)

You can check your answer by listing all 6 different kinds of pizza:

mushroom/pepperoni	pepperoni/sausage	mushroom/cheese
mushroom/sausage	pepperoni/cheese	sausage/cheese

Guidelines: • The Counting Principle can be applied to three or more events.

EXERCISES

1. You have 5 pair of jeans and 6 sweatshirts. Use the Counting Principle to find the number of different outfits you can wear by choosing 1 pair of jeans and 1 sweatshirt.

2. Use Pascal's Triangle to find the number of ways you can order a pizza if you choose 3 toppings from 5 possible pizza toppings.

Reteach

Chapter 8

Name _____

What you should learn:

8.8	Compare theoretical and experimental probabilities and how to find the probability of a multistage event

Correlation to Pupil's Textbook:

Chapter Test (p. 387)
Exercises 12, 13, 19, 20

Examples | *Comparing Probabilities and The Probability of a Multistage Event*

a. Your state lottery is designed so that each player chooses 7 digits. How many different "numbers" are possible? What is the probability that your "number" is drawn by the lottery officials?

For each of the 7 digits, you have 10 choices. Thus, the number of different "numbers" is

$$10 \cdot 10 \cdot 10 \cdot 10 \cdot 10 \cdot 10 \cdot 10 = 10^7 = 10,000,000.$$

The probability that your "number" is drawn by the lottery officials is

$$\text{Probability} = \frac{1}{10,000,000}.$$

b. A six-sided die is rolled, then a coin is tossed. Find the probability that the outcome is the number 5 and tails.

There are 6 outcomes for rolling a die and 2 outcomes for tossing a coin. The "number" of different outcomes is $6 \cdot 2$ or 12 outcomes.

Because there are 12 different outcomes, the probability that the outcome is the number 5 and tails is

$$\text{Probability} = \frac{1}{12}.$$

Guidelines:

- You can use the Counting Principle to compare probabilities and to find the probability of a multistage event.

EXERCISES

In Exercises 1–6, a coin is tossed, then a six-sided die is rolled. Find the probability of the indicated outcome.

1. Heads and an odd number

2. Heads and a number greater than 4

3. Tails and 6

4. Heads and 2

5. Tails and a number less than 6

6. Tails and an even number

Reteach
Chapter 9

Name _____

What you should learn:

9.1	How to solve equations whose solutions are square roots and how to use square roots to solve real-life problems

Correlation to Pupil's Textbook:

Mid-Chapter Self-Test (p. 409)   Chapter Test (p. 433)
Exercises 1–6   Exercises 1–3

Examples	*Using the Square Root Property and Modeling Real-Life Problems*

a. Use square roots to solve $n^2 - 1 = 48$.

$$n^2 - 1 = 48 \qquad \textit{Original equation}$$
$$n^2 - 1 + 1 = 48 + 1 \qquad \textit{Add 1 to each side.}$$
$$n^2 = 49 \qquad \textit{Simplify.}$$
$$n = -\sqrt{49} \qquad -\sqrt{49} \textit{ or } -7 \textit{ is one solution.}$$
$$n = \sqrt{49} \qquad \sqrt{49} \textit{ or } 7 \textit{ is the other solution.}$$

There are two solutions: -7 and 7.

b. A square flower garden has an area of 100 square feet. What are the dimensions of the garden?

Verbal
Model $\qquad$ $\boxed{\text{Area of Square}} = \left(\boxed{\text{Length of side}} \right)^2$

Labels $\qquad$ Area of square $= 100 \qquad$ (square feet)
$\qquad\qquad$ Length of side $= s \qquad$ (feet)

Algebraic
Model $\qquad$ $100 = s^2 \qquad$ *Write algebraic model.*
$\qquad\qquad$ $10 = s \qquad$ *Choose positive square root.*

The length of each side of the garden is 10 feet.

Guidelines:

- If a is a positive number, then $x^2 = a$ has two solutions.

  1. $x = -\sqrt{a}$ is a solution because $\left(-\sqrt{a} \right)^2 = a$.
  2. $x = \sqrt{a}$ is a solution because $\left(\sqrt{a} \right)^2 = a$.

- When you use the square root property to solve for length, choose only the positive solution (length must be positive).

EXERCISES

In Exercises 1–8, write both square roots of the number.

1. 26 $\qquad$ **2.** 196 $\qquad$ **3.** 47 $\qquad$ **4.** 324

5. $\frac{9}{49}$ $\qquad$ **6.** 0.64 $\qquad$ **7.** $\frac{16}{81}$ $\qquad$ **8.** 900

In Exercises 9–12, write both solutions of the equation. Round each solution to three decimal places, if necessary.

9. $n^2 = 4$ $\qquad$ **10.** $x^2 = 21$ $\qquad$ **11.** $2y^2 = 18$ $\qquad$ **12.** $9a^2 = 16$

13. A square sandbox has an area of 36 square feet. What are the dimensions of the sandbox?

What you should learn:

9.2	How to classify real numbers as rational or irrational and how to represent real numbers with a number line

Correlation to Pupil's Textbook:

Mid-Chapter Self-Test (p. 409)
Exercises 7–12

Chapter Test (p. 433)
Exercises 5–8

Examples | *Classifying Real Numbers and Using a Number Line*

a. For each number, give its decimal form and decimal type. Then classify each number as rational or irrational.

Number	Decimal Form	Decimal Type	Classification
$\frac{1}{9}$	$0.\overline{1}$	repeating	rational
$\sqrt{5}$	$2.23606797\ldots$	nonrepeating	irrational
$\frac{7}{2}$	3.5	terminating	rational

b. Plot the pair of numbers, $\sqrt{7}$ and $\frac{13}{5}$, on a number line by first writing each number in decimal form. Complete the statement $\sqrt{7}$ $\boxed{?}$ $\frac{13}{5}$ with $<$, $>$, or $=$.

$$\sqrt{7} \approx 2.646 \text{ and } \frac{13}{5} = 2.6$$

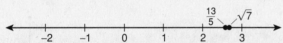

Because $\sqrt{7}$ is to the right of $\frac{13}{5}$, you can conclude that $\sqrt{7} > \frac{13}{5}$.

Guidelines:

- Irrational numbers are numbers that cannot be written as the quotient of two integers.
- Together, the set of all rational numbers and irrational numbers make up the set of real numbers.
- The decimal form of a rational number either terminates or repeats.
- The decimal form of an irrational number does not repeat or terminate.

EXERCISES

In Exercises 1–4, give the decimal form and decimal type. Determine whether the number is rational or irrational.

1. $\sqrt{13}$ **2.** $\sqrt{0.36}$ **3.** $\frac{1}{11}$ **4.** $-\sqrt{\frac{25}{4}}$

In Exercises 5–8, match the number with its graph.

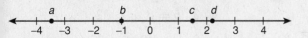

5. $-\sqrt{12}$ **6.** $\sqrt{4.82}$ **7.** $\dfrac{-\sqrt{16}}{4}$ **8.** $\sqrt{\dfrac{36}{16}}$

What you should learn:

9.3	How to use the Pythagorean Theorem and how to solve a right triangle

Correlation to Pupil's Textbook:

Mid-Chapter Self-Test (p. 409) Chapter Test (p. 433)
Exercises 13–16   Exercises 9–11

Examples   *Using the Pythagorean Theorem and Solving a Right Triangle*

a. Use the Pythagorean Theorem to find the distance between the shopping mall and the airport, as shown at the right.

For any right triangle, the sum of the squares of the lengths of the legs, a and b, equals the square of the length of the hypotenuse, c.

$a^2 + b^2 = c^2$ *Pythagorean Theorem*

$3^2 + 4^2 = c^2$ *Substitute for a and b.*

$25 = c^2$ *Simplify.*

$5 = c$ *Square Root Property*

The distance between the shopping mall and the airport is 5 miles.

b. In $\triangle PQR$, $q = 10$ and $p = 7$. Use the Pythagorean Theorem to find the length of the other leg, r. Is the triangle isosceles?

$p^2 + r^2 = q^2$ *Pythagorean Theorem*

$7^2 + r^2 = 10^2$ *Substitute for p and q.*

$49 + r^2 = 100$ *Simplify.*

$r^2 = 51$ *Subtract 49 from each side.*

$r = \sqrt{51}$ *Square Root Property*

$r \approx 7.14$ *Use a calculator.*

The triangle is not isosceles because the legs do not have the same length.

Guidelines:
- A right triangle is a triangle that has a right angle (one whose measure is $90°$).
- The sides that form the right angle are the legs of the triangle, and the other side is the hypotenuse.
- Using the lengths of two sides of a right triangle to find the length of the third side is called solving a right triangle.

EXERCISES

In Exercises 1–6, a and b are the lengths of the legs of a right triangle, and c is the length of the hypotenuse. Find the missing length.

1. $a = 4, b = 9$ **2.** $a = 8, c = 17$ **3.** $b = 5, c = 32$

4. $a = 7, b = 3$ **5.** $b = 5, c = 5\sqrt{2}$ **6.** $a = 18, c = 82$

Reteach
Chapter 9

What you should learn:

9.4 How to use properties of triangles to solve real-life problems and how to use the Pythagorean Theorem to measure indirectly

Correlation to Pupil's Textbook:

Mid-Chapter Self-Test (p. 409)   Chapter Test (p. 433)
Exercises 17–20   Exercises 4, 18, 19

Examples   *Modeling Real-Life Problems and Indirect Measurement*

a. Find the perimeter and the area of the figure shown at the right.

You can use the Pythagorean Theorem to find the length of the leg, a.

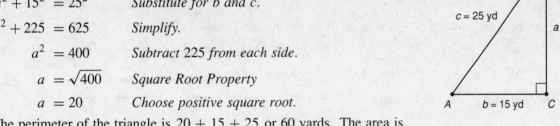

$a^2 + b^2 = c^2$ *Pythagorean Theorem*

$a^2 + 15^2 = 25^2$ *Substitute for b and c.*

$a^2 + 225 = 625$ *Simplify.*

$a^2 = 400$ *Subtract 225 from each side.*

$a = \sqrt{400}$ *Square Root Property*

$a = 20$ *Choose positive square root.*

The perimeter of the triangle is $20 + 15 + 25$ or 60 yards. The area is $\frac{1}{2}ab = \frac{1}{2}(20)(15) = 150$ square yards.

b. You ride your bike from your home to your friend's home. You ride 8 miles due north, then ride 7 miles due east, as shown at the right. Find the shortest distance between the two homes.

You can use the Pythagorean Theorem to find the length of the hypotenuse, which is the shortest distance between the two homes.

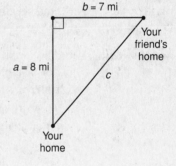

$a^2 + b^2 = c^2$ *Pythagorean Theorem*

$8^2 + 7^2 = c^2$ *Substitute for a and b.*

$64 + 49 = c^2$ *Simplify.*

$113 = c^2$ *Simplify.*

$\sqrt{113} = c$ *Square Root Property*

$10.6 \approx c$ *Use a calculator.*

The shortest distance between the two homes is about 10.6 miles.

Guidelines: • The Pythagorean Theorem can be used to measure objects indirectly.

EXERCISE

1. A 45-foot tree casts a shadow 24 feet long, as shown at the right. Find the distance, c, from the top of the tree to the tip of the shadow.

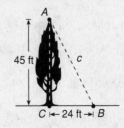

Reteach

Chapter 9

Name _____

What you should learn:

9.5	How to graph an inequality and how to write equivalent inequalities

Correlation to Pupil's Textbook:

Chapter Test (p. 433)

Exercises 12–14

Examples | *Graphing Inequalities and Writing Equivalent Inequalities*

a. Graph the inequality $x \leq 1$.

Plot the number 1 with a closed dot to show that 1 is included. Then shade the part of the number line that is to the left of 1.

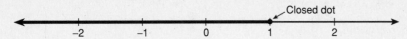

b. Write an inequality for the verbal phrase. Then graph each inequality.

Verbal Phrase   Inequality   Graph

All real numbers greater than -1. $x > -1$

All real numbers less than or equal to 3. $x \leq 3$

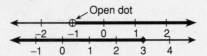

c. Write an equivalent inequality for $a \leq 5$. Then state the inequality verbally.

The inequality $a \leq 5$ is equivalent to $5 \geq a$. Either inequality can be written verbally as "the set of all real numbers less than or equal to 5."

Guidelines:

- The graph of an inequality on a number line is either an open dot or a closed dot, with part of the number line shaded to the right or to the left of the dot.
- To write an inequality that is equivalent to $a < b$, move each letter to the other side, and reverse the inequality. $a < b \Rightarrow b > a$
- One way to check that two inequalities are equivalent is to be sure that the inequality symbols "point" toward the same number or variable.

EXERCISES

In Exercises 1–4, graph the inequality.

1. $x < 4$ **2.** $x \geq -2$ **3.** $x > 0$ **4.** $x \leq -3$

In Exercises 5–7, solve the inequality. Then graph the solution.

5. $n + 2 \leq 3$ **6.** $-2 < x - 1$ **7.** $z + 10 \geq 6$

In Exercises 8–10, write an equivalent inequality.

8. $a < -8$ **9.** $t \geq 0$ **10.** $w \leq 7$

Reteach
Chapter 9

Name _____

What you should learn:

9.6 How to use properties of inequalities and how to use multiplication and division to solve an inequality

Correlation to Pupil's Textbook:

Chapter Test (p. 433)

Exercises 15, 17

Examples   *Using Properties of Inequalities and Solving Inequalities*

a. Use the properties of inequalities to solve $8 \geq -4x$.

$8 \geq -4x$ *Original inequality*

$\dfrac{8}{-4} \leq \dfrac{-4x}{-4}$ *Divide each side by −4 and reverse the direction of the inequality symbol.*

$-2 \leq x$ *Simplify.*

The solution is $-2 \leq x$, which is the set of all real numbers that are greater than or equal to −2.

b. You are paid $2.50 per hour to babysit. How many hours of babysitting will earn you at least $35?

Let n represent the number of hours. Then your total pay is $2.50n$.

$2.50n \geq 35$ *Pay is at least $35.*

$\dfrac{2.50n}{2.50} \geq \dfrac{35}{2.50}$ *Divide each side by 2.50.*

$n \geq 14$ *Simplify.*

You will earn at least $35 if you babysit at least 14 hours.

Guidelines:

- Adding or subtracting the same number on each side of an inequality produces an equivalent inequality.

- Multiplying or dividing each side of an inequality by the same positive number produces an equivalent inequality.

- Multiplying or dividing each side of an inequality by the same negative number and reversing the direction of the inequality symbol produces an equivalent inequality.

EXERCISES

In Exercises 1–8, solve the inequality. Then graph the solution.

1. $6y \geq -18$

2. $\dfrac{x}{3} < -1$

3. $-70 > 7a$

4. $-3n \leq 15$

5. $2 \geq \dfrac{-1}{4}s$

6. $3.5x > 10.5$

7. $\dfrac{-3}{8} < \dfrac{-3}{4}b$

8. $\dfrac{t}{-2} \leq 3$

What you should learn:

9.7	How to solve multistep inequalities and how to use multistep inequalities to solve real-life problems

Correlation to Pupil's Textbook:

Chapter Test (p. 433)
Exercises 16, 20

Examples *Solving Multistep Inequalities and Solving Real-Life Problems*

a. Solve $-3x - 4 \geq 8$.

$$-3x - 4 \geq 8 \qquad \textit{Rewrite original inequality.}$$
$$-3x - 4 + 4 \geq 8 + 4 \qquad \textit{Add 4 to each side.}$$
$$-3x \geq 12 \qquad \textit{Simplify.}$$
$$\frac{-3x}{-3} \leq \frac{12}{-3} \qquad \textit{Divide each side by } -3 \textit{ and reverse the direction of the inequality symbol.}$$
$$x \leq -4 \qquad \textit{Simplify.}$$

The solution is all real numbers that are less than or equal to -4.

b. You are going to a movie. The admission price is $6, and soft drinks cost $1.25. You don't want to spend more than $10. Write an inequality that describes the number of soft drinks that you can buy. Then solve the inequality.

Verbal
Model

6 dollars	+	Cost of a soft drink	·	Number of soft drinks	≤	10 dollars

Labels   Cost of a soft drink $= 1.25$ (dollars)
            Number of soft drinks $= x$

Algebraic $6 + 1.25x \leq 10$
Model
                    $1.25x \leq 4$

                        $x \leq 3.2$

You can buy up to 3 soft drinks.

Guidelines:

- You can use the addition, subtraction, multiplication, and division properties of inequalities to solve inequalities that require two or more steps.
- If you multiply or divide by a negative number, you must reverse the direction of the inequality symbol.

EXERCISES

In Exercises 1–6, solve the inequality.

1. $12x - 5 \geq 31$ **2.** $-2a + 4 < -12$ **3.** $3y - 8 > -5y$

4. $-\frac{1}{3}n \leq \frac{5}{3}n + 10$ **5.** $2(4 + x) \geq 10$ **6.** $3(2x - 1) < 3x + 6$

7. You charge $4.50 per hour to mow lawns. If you spend $5.25 on gas for the mower, how many hours must you mow to earn a profit of at least $30?

What you should learn:

9.8 How to use the Triangle Inequality

Correlation to Pupil's Textbook:

Chapter Test (p. 433)
Exercise 18

| **Examples** | *Using the Triangle Inequality* |

a. For triangle PQR shown at the right, use the Triangle Inequality to write three inequalities.

The sum of the lengths of any two sides of a triangle is greater than the length of the third side. In $\triangle PQR$, you can write

$$p + q > r$$
$$q + r > p$$
$$p + r > q.$$

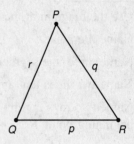

b. The measures of two sides of a triangle are 12 and 15. What can you say about the measure of the third side?

Begin by drawing a diagram with the sides 12, 15 and x. From the triangle, you can write the following inequalities:

$$12 + x > 15 \text{ and } 12 + 15 > x.$$

By solving these two inequalities, you can determine that the measure of the third side is more than 3 ($x > 3$) and less than 27 ($x < 27$).

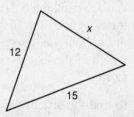

Guidelines:

- The sum of the lengths of any two sides of a triangle is greater than the length of the third side.

EXERCISES

In Exercises 1–4, use the figure at the right to complete the statement.

1. $s + q > \boxed{?}$

2. $r < p + \boxed{?} + t$

3. $r < \boxed{?} + p$

4. $p + q + r > \boxed{?}$

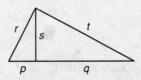

In Exercises 5–7, the measures of two sides of a triangle are given. What can you say about the measure of the third side?

5. 9 and 14

6. 10 and 18

7. 7 and 11

What you should learn:

10.1	How to identify points, lines, and planes in real-life situations and how to use geometry to solve real-life problems

Correlation to Pupil's Textbook:

Mid-Chapter Self-Test (p. 461)   **Chapter Test (p. 485)**

Exercises 1–4   Exercises 9, 10

Examples | *Identifying Points, Lines, and Planes and Solving Real-Life Problems*

a. Use the diagram at the right for each of the following.

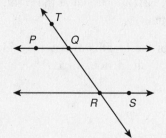

Name the points. P, Q, R, S, T

Name three line segments on $\overleftrightarrow{TR}$. $\overline{QT}, \overline{QR}, \overline{RT}$

Name two lines that appear parallel. $\overleftrightarrow{PQ}$ and $\overleftrightarrow{RS}$

Name two rays that have the same $\overrightarrow{RQ}$ and $\overrightarrow{RS}$
beginning point R.

b. You are planning a delivery route through 4 cities. You must start at city A and stop first at city B. Your next stop is either city C or city D, but you must stop at both cities before returning to city A. Which of the two routes shown in the diagrams at the right is the shortest?

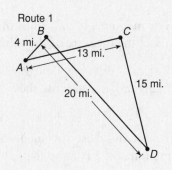

To find the distance along each route, add the lengths of the line segments that make up the route.

The distance along Route 1 is $4 + 20 + 15 + 13 = 52$ miles.
The distance along Route 2 is $4 + 10 + 15 + 18 = 47$ miles.
Route 2 is the shortest route.

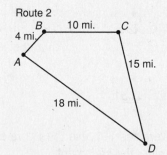

Guidelines:

- The length of the line segment $\overline{KL}$ is denoted by KL.
- Two lines are parallel if they lie in the same plane and do not intersect.

EXERCISES

In Exercises 1–4, use the diagram at the right.

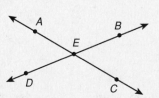

1. Write two other names for the line $\overleftrightarrow{EC}$.

2. Name 4 rays that have the same beginning point.

3. Name a point of intersection of two lines.

4. Name 3 different line segments that lie on $\overleftrightarrow{DB}$.

Reteach
Chapter 10

Name _____

What you should learn:

10.2	How to identify angles as acute, right, obtuse, or straight

Correlation to Pupil's Textbook:

Mid-Chapter Self-Test (p. 461) **Chapter Test (p. 485)**
Exercises 5–8   Exercises 6–8, 19

Examples | *Identifying Angles*

a. Use the figure at the right to match each of the following.

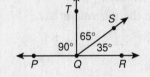

1. ∠PQR [d]   a. right angle (measures 90°)
2. ∠SQR [c]   b. obtuse angle (measures between 90° and 180°)
3. ∠PQS [b]   c. acute angle (measures between 0° and 90°)
4. ∠PQT [a]   d. straight angle (measures 180°)

b. Name two congruent angles in the figure at the right.

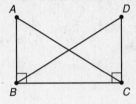

Two angles are congruent if they have the same measure. Each right angle, ∠ABC and ∠DCB, measures 90°, thus they are congruent.

Guidelines:

- An angle consists of two rays that begin at the same point.
- The measure of ∠A is denoted by $m\angle A$.
- A protractor can be used to approximate the measure of an angle.
- Two lines that meet at a right angle are perpendicular.

EXERCISES

In Exercises 1–4, match each angle with the description.

a. acute   b. obtuse   c. right   d. straight

1.   2.   3.   4.

In Exercises 5–8, use the figure at the right.

5. List the straight angles in the figure.

6. List the right angles in the figure.

7. List the acute angles in the figure.

8. List the obtuse angle in the figure.

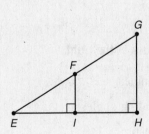

Reteach
Chapter 10

Name _____

Correlation to Pupil's Textbook:

Mid-Chapter Self-Test (p. 461)   **Chapter Test (p. 485)**
Exercises 9–12   Exercises 11, 13, 18, 20

What you should learn:

10.3	How to identify angles formed when two parallel lines intersect a third line and how to use properties of parallel lines to solve real-life problems

Examples — *Using Properties of Parallel Lines and Solving Real-Life Problems*

a. In the diagram at the right, identify all congruent vertical angles.

   $\angle 1 \cong \angle 2$, $\angle 3 \cong \angle 4$ Vertical angles

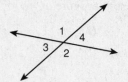

b. In the diagram at the right, identify all congruent corresponding angles.

   $\angle 1 \cong \angle 3$, $\angle 2 \cong \angle 4$ Corresponding angles
   $\angle 5 \cong \angle 7$, $\angle 6 \cong \angle 8$ Corresponding angles

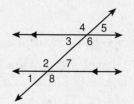

c. In the diagram at the right, Chestnut Street is parallel to Elm Street, and both are intersected by Main Street. The measure of $\angle 1$ is $45°$. Find the measure of $\angle 3$.

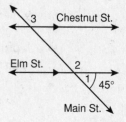

Because $\angle 1$ and $\angle 2$ combined form a straight angle, the sum of their measures is $180°$. Thus,

$$m\angle 2 = 180° - m\angle 1 = 180° - 45° = 135°.$$

Because $\angle 2$ and $\angle 3$ are corresponding angles, they are congruent and must have the same measure. Thus, $m\angle 3 = m\angle 2 = 135°$.

Guidelines: • Vertical angles are congruent.

   • When two parallel lines are intersected by a third line, the corresponding angles are congruent. (If the lines are not parallel, then the corresponding angles are not congruent.)

EXERCISES

In Exercises 1–4, use the figure at the right.

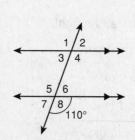

1. List all pairs of vertical angles.

2. List all pairs of corresponding angles.

3. List all angles whose measure is $110°$.

4. List all angles whose measure is $70°$.

Reteach
Chapter 10

Name _____

What you should learn:

10.4	How to identify line symmetry and how to identify rotational symmetry

Correlation to Pupil's Textbook:

Mid-Chapter Self-Test (p. 461)
Exercises 13–15

Chapter Test (p. 485)
Exercise 14

Examples — *Identifying Line Symmetry and Identifying Rotational Symmetry*

a. Identify the line of symmetry in the figure at the right.

This figure has a vertical line of symmetry.

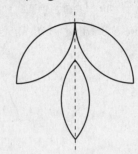

b. Identify any rotational symmetry in the figure.

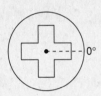 

This figure has rotational symmetry.
It will coincide with itself after being
rotated 90° or 180° in either direction.

Guidelines:

- A figure has line symmetry if it can be divided by a line into two parts, each of which is the mirror image of the other.

- A figure has rotational symmetry if it coincides with itself after rotating 180° or less, either clockwise or counterclockwise about a point.

EXERCISES

In Exercises 1–4, identify any symmetry of the figure.

1.

2.

3.

4.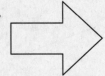

What you should learn:

10.5	How to identify triangles by their sides and how to identify triangles by their angles

Correlation to Pupil's Textbook:

Mid-Chapter Self-Test (p. 461)   **Chapter Test (p. 485)**
Exercises 16–20   Exercises 1–3

Examples | *Identifying Triangles by Their Sides and Identifying Triangles by Their Angles*

a. Classify each triangle according to its sides.

$\triangle XYZ$ is equilateral because it has three sides of length 5.

$\triangle EFG$ is scalene because all three sides have different lengths.

$\triangle JKL$ is isosceles because it has two sides of length 6.

b. Classify each triangle according to its angles.

  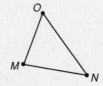

$\triangle ABC$ is equiangular because all three angles have the same measure.

$\triangle RST$ is right because one of its angles is a right angle.

$\triangle MNO$ is acute because all three angles are acute.

$\triangle PQR$ is obtuse because one of its angles is obtuse.

Guidelines:

- Triangles are classified by their sides into three categories - scalene, isosceles and equilateral.
- Triangles are classified by their angles into four categories - acute, equiangular, obtuse, and right.

EXERCISES

In Exercises 1–4, classify the triangle according to its sides and angles.

1.
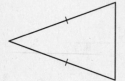

2.

3.

4.
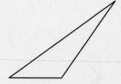

Reteach
Chapter 10

Name _____

What you should learn:

10.6	How to identify quadrilaterals

Example | *Identifying Quadrilaterals*

a. Classify each quadrilateral by matching it with the correct description.

1. Parallelogram   [f]   a. A quadrilateral with only one pair of parallel sides.

2. Rectangle   [e]   b. A parallelogram with sides of equal length.

3. Square   [g]   c. A quadrilateral with all sides having different lengths.

4. Rhombus   [b]   d. A quadrilateral that is not a parallelogram, but has two pair of sides of equal length.

5. Trapezoid   [a]   e. A parallelogram with four right angles.

6. Kite   [d]   f. A quadrilateral with opposite sides parallel.

7. Scalene Quadrilateral   [c]   g. A rectangle with sides of equal length.

Guidelines:

- A trapezoid is isosceles if its nonparallel sides have the same length.

- A quadrilateral is convex if a segment joining any two interior points lies completely within the quadrilateral.

EXERCISES

In Exercises 1–3, identify the quadrilateral from its appearance.
Use the name that best describes the quadrilateral.

1.

2.

3.
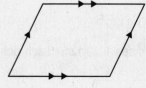

In Exercises 4–7, complete the statement with **always, sometimes,** or **never.**

4. A parallelogram is [?] a quadrilateral.

5. A kite is [?] a rhombus.

6. A rectangle is [?] a square.

7. A square is [?] a rhombus.

What you should learn:

10.7	How to recognize congruent polygons and how to identify regular polygons

Correlation to Pupil's Textbook:

Chapter Test (p. 485)
Exercises 4, 12, 13

Examples	*Recognizing Congruent Polygons and Identifying Regular Polygons*

a. Two polygons are congruent if they are exactly the same size and shape. Which of the polygons below are congruent to the polygon at the right?

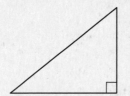

Not congruent–not the same size

Congruent–same size and shape

Not congruent–not the same shape

b. A polygon is regular if each of its sides has the same length and each of its angles has the same measure. Which of the polygons below are regular?

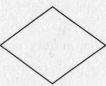
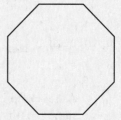

Not regular–each side does not have the same length.

Not regular–each angle does not have the same measure.

Regular–each side has the same length and each angle has the same measure.

Guidelines: • To decide whether two polygons are congruent, you can trace each on paper, cut one out, and try to move the cut polygon so that it lies exactly on top of the other polygon.

EXERCISES

In Exercises 1–3, name each polygon. Is the polygon regular?

1.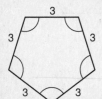

2.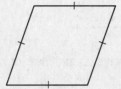

3.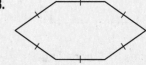

Reteach
Chapter 10

Name _____

What you should learn:

10.8	How to find the measures of the angles of a polygon and how to find the measure of each angle of a regular polygon

Correlation to Pupil's Textbook:

Chapter Test (p. 485)
Exercises 15, 16

Examples | *Measuring the Angles of a Polygon and Measuring Angles in a Regular Polygon*

a. Find the measures of $\angle 1$ and $\angle 2$ for the polygon shown at the right.

For a polygon with n sides, the sum of the measures of the interior angles is $(n-2)(180°)$. For $n = 3$, the sum of the angles is $180°$. You are given that $m\angle 3 = 40°$ and $m\angle 5 = 110°$. It follows that

$$m\angle 1 = 180° - (40° + 110°)$$
$$= 180° - 150°$$
$$= 30°.$$

Because $\angle 1$ and $\angle 2$ combine to form a straight angle,

$$m\angle 1 + m\angle 2 = 180°$$
$$30° + m\angle 2 = 180°$$
$$m\angle 2 = 150°.$$

b. Find the sum of the measures of the interior angles of a regular hexagon. Then find the measure of each interior angle.

For a polygon with n sides, the sum of the interior angle measures is $(n-2)(180°)$. For $n = 6$, the sum is $4(180°) = 720°$. For a regular polygon, each interior angle measures $\dfrac{(n-2)(180°)}{n}$.

For $n = 6$, each interior angle measures $\dfrac{4(180°)}{6} = 120°$.

c. Find the sum of the measures of the exterior angles of a regular hexagon. Then find the measure of each exterior angle.

The sum of the exterior angle measures of any polygon is $360°$. For a regular polygon, each exterior angle measures $\dfrac{360°}{n}$.

For $n = 6$, each exterior angle measures $\dfrac{360°}{6} = 60°$.

Guidelines:

- The angles of a polygon are called interior angles.
- Polygons also have exterior angles, each of which combines with an interior angle to form a straight angle.

EXERCISE

Find the measures of $\angle 4$ and $\angle 6$ in Example a above.

Name _____

What you should learn:

| 10.9 | How to compare side lengths and angle measures of a triangle and how to find the angle measures of an isosceles triangle |

Correlation to Pupil's Textbook:

Chapter Test (p. 485)

Exercise 17

| **Examples** | *Angles and Sides of Triangles and Comparing Angles in Isosceles Triangles* |

a. In the triangle at the right, without using a protractor, state which angle is the largest and which is the smallest.

In a triangle, the longest side is opposite the largest angle. The longest side is $\overline{PR}$. This implies that the largest angle is $\angle Q$.

Also, in a triangle, the shortest side is opposite the smallest angle. The shortest side is $\overline{PQ}$; therefore, the smallest angle is $\angle R$.

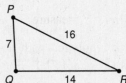

b. In the triangle at the right, name two angles that have equal measures.

In an isosceles triangle, the angles opposite the sides of the same lengths have equal measures. Since sides $\overline{AB}$ and $\overline{AC}$ have the same length, 7, $\angle B$ and $\angle C$ have the same measure.

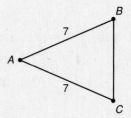

Guidelines:

- In a triangle, the longest side is opposite the largest angle and the shortest side is opposite the smallest angle.

- In an isosceles triangle, the angles opposite the sides of the same lengths have equal measures.

EXERCISES

In Exercises 1–3, identify the smallest angle, largest angle, shortest side, and longest side.

1.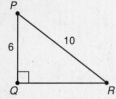

2.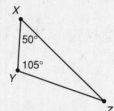

3.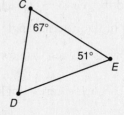

In Exercises 4–6, use the figure at the right to find the measure of the angle.

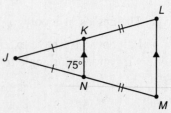

4. $m\angle JKN$

5. $m\angle JML$

6. $m\angle NJK$

Reteach
Chapter 11

Name _____

What you should learn:

11.1	How to find the area and perimeter of polygons and how to use area and perimeter to solve real-life problems

Correlation to Pupil's Textbook:

Mid-Chapter Self-Test (p. 510)   **Chapter Test (p. 535)**
Exercises 13–16   Exercises 1–3

| **Examples** | *Finding Area and Perimeter and Solving Real-Life Problems* |

a. Find the area and the perimeter of the trapezoid at the right.

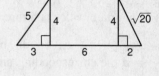

For the trapezoid, the height is $h = 4$ and the lengths of the bases are $b_1 = 6$ and $b_2 = 11$.

Area $= \frac{1}{2}(b_1 + b_2)h = \frac{1}{2}(6 + 11)4 = 34$. The area of the trapezoid is 34 square units.

You can find the perimeter of the trapezoid by adding the lengths of the four sides. Perimeter $= 6 + \sqrt{20} + 11 + 5 \approx 26.5$ units.

b. You are designing a small slate patio. Each of the 52 pieces of slate is a parallelogram with base 7 inches and height 5 inches. Find the area of the patio.

For each parallelogram, Area $=$ (base)(height) $= (7)(5) = 35$ square inches.

The total area of the patio is 52 times the area of each parallelogram. Total area $= 52 \cdot 35 = 1820$ square inches.

Guidelines:
- The Area of a Parallelogram: Area $=$ (base) $\times$ (height).
- The Area of a Trapezoid: Area $= \frac{1}{2}$ (base 1 $+$ base 2) $\times$ (height).

EXERCISES

In Exercises 1–3, find the area and the perimeter of each figure.

1.

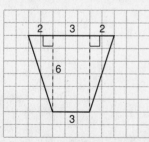

2.

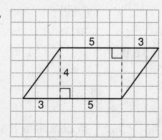

3.

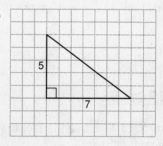

4. Find the area of each figure. Describe two ways to find the area of the second figure.

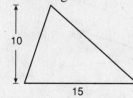
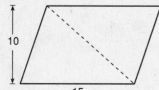

Name _____

What you should learn:

11.2	How to determine whether two figures are congruent and how to use congruence to solve real-life problems

Correlation to Pupil's Textbook:

Mid-Chapter Self-Test (p. 510)   **Chapter Test (p. 535)**
Exercises 1–4   Exercise 20

Examples	*Congruence and Measure and Using Congruence in Real Life*

a. Triangles PQR and XYZ at the right are congruent. Name three pairs of congruent sides and three pairs of congruent angles.

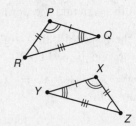

$\triangle PQR \cong \triangle XYZ$ if and only if the corresponding sides are congruent and the corresponding angles are congruent.

Corresponding Sides   Corresponding Angles

$\overline{PQ} \cong \overline{XY}$ $\angle P \cong \angle X$

$\overline{QR} \cong \overline{YZ}$ $\angle Q \cong \angle Y$

$\overline{RP} \cong \overline{ZX}$ $\angle R \cong \angle Z$

b. You are making two triangular banners from a piece of cloth which is a parallelogram in shape. Parallelogram $ABCD$ is shown at the right. Show that the two banners are congruent by naming two congruent triangles formed by drawing diagonal $\overline{AC}$.

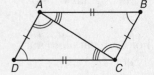

You can conclude that $\triangle ABC \cong \triangle CDA$ because corresponding sides and angles are congruent.

Corresponding Sides   Corresponding Angles

$\overline{CB} \cong \overline{AD}$ $\angle B \cong \angle D$

$\overline{AB} \cong \overline{CD}$ $\angle BAC \cong \angle DCA$

$\overline{AC} \cong \overline{CA}$ $\angle BCA \cong \angle DAC$

Guidelines: • Congruent line segments have the same length.

                     • Congruent angles have the same measure.

                     • Congruent triangles have the same size and shape.

EXERCISES

In Exercises 1–6, use the fact that $\triangle CDE \cong \triangle JKL$ to complete the statement.

1. $\angle E \cong$ [?]   **2.** $\overline{CE} \cong$ [?]   **3.** [?] $\cong \angle J$

4. [?] $\cong \overline{JK}$ **5.** $\overline{DE} \cong$ [?]   **6.** $\angle D \cong$ [?]

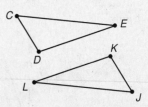

Name _____

What you should learn:

| 11.3 | How to reflect a figure about a line and how to use properties of reflections |

Correlation to Pupil's Textbook:

Mid-Chapter Self-Test (p. 510) Chapter Test (p. 535)
Exercises 5, 6   Exercises 4, 8

Examples | *Reflecting Figures about Lines and Reflections and Line Symmetry*

a. $\triangle PQR$ is reflected about the x-axis, as shown at the right. Name the image of $\triangle PQR$. Name a triangle that is congruent to $\triangle PQR$.

The image of $\triangle PQR$ is $\triangle P'Q'R'$.

When a figure is reflected about a line, the image is congruent to the original figure. Thus, $\triangle PQR \cong \triangle P'Q'R'$.

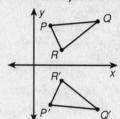

b. In the figure at the right, $\triangle ABC$ is reflected about line p. Name 3 line segments that are perpendicular to line p and also are bisected by line p.

In a reflection, the reflection line p is perpendicular to and bisects each segment that joins an original point to its image. Thus, line p is perpendicular to $\overline{AA'}$, $\overline{BB'}$, and $\overline{CC'}$. Line p also bisects $\overline{AA'}$, $\overline{BB'}$, and $\overline{CC'}$.

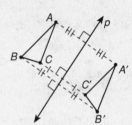

c. Triangle EFG is reflected about $\overleftrightarrow{FG}$. Identify the line symmetry in quadrilateral $FEGE'$.

In quadrilateral $FEGE'$, reflection line $\overleftrightarrow{FG}$ is a horizontal line of symmetry.

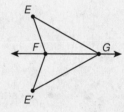

Guidelines: • Properties of Line Reflections:
1. When a figure is reflected about a line, the image is congruent to the original figure.
2. In a reflection, the reflection line is perpendicular to and bisects each segment that joins an original point to its image.

EXERCISES

In Exercises 1–4, name the image of $\triangle RST$ after the indicated reflection(s).

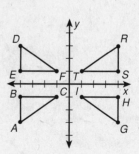

1. Reflect $\triangle RST$ about the y-axis.

2. Reflect $\triangle RST$ about the x-axis.

3. Reflect $\triangle RST$ about the y-axis, then about the x-axis.

4. Reflect $\triangle RST$ about the x-axis, then about the y-axis.

Reteach
Chapter 11

Name _____

What you should learn:

11.4	How to rotate a figure about a point and how to use properties of rotations to answer questions about real-life situations

Correlation to Pupil's Textbook:

Mid-Chapter Self-Test (p. 510)   **Chapter Test (p. 535)**
Exercises 7, 8, 17–20   Exercises 5, 6, 9

Examples   *Rotating Figures about Points and Properties of Rotations*

a. $\triangle XYZ$ is rotated about the origin to become $\triangle X'Y'Z'$. Find the angle of rotation. Find the vertices of the original figure and the image.

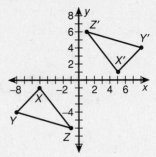

$\triangle XYZ$ is rotated counterclockwise $180°$. The vertices of the original figure and the image are as follows.

$X\ (-5, -1),\quad Y\ (-8, -4),\quad Z\ (-1, -6)$
$X'\ (5, 1),\quad\ \ Y'\ (8, 4),\quad\ \ Z'\ (1, 6)$

b. The figure at the right has been rotated as indicated. Estimate the angle and direction of the rotation.

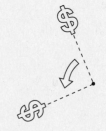

The rotation is $90°$ in a counterclockwise direction.

Guidelines:
- Rotating a figure produces a congruent figure.
- If a figure has rotational symmetry, then it can be rotated about a point so that the image coincides with the original figure.

EXERCISES

In Exercises 1–3, estimate the angle and direction of rotation.

1.

2.

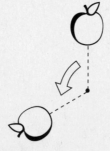

3.

What you should learn:

11.5	How to translate a figure in a plane and how to represent translations in a coordinate plane

Correlation to Pupil's Textbook:

Mid-Chapter Self-Test (p. 510)   **Chapter Test (p. 535)**
Exercises 9–12   Exercises 7, 10, 11

Examples	*Translating Figures in a Plane and Translating in a Coordinate Plane*

a. Describe the translation verbally.

This figure has been translated 6 units to the left and 3 units up.

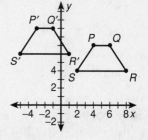

b. The vertices of trapezoid $PQRS$ are $P(4, 7)$, $Q(6, 7)$, $R(8, 4)$, and $S(2, 4)$. Use the following motion rule to translate each vertex.

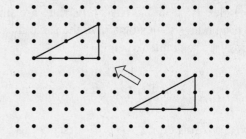

Original Figure	Image
(x, y)	$(x - 7, y + 2)$

The motion rule tells you to subtract 7 from each x-coordinate and add 2 to each y-coordinate.

Original Figure	Image
$P(4, 7)$	$P'(-3, 9)$
$Q(6, 7)$	$Q'(-1, 9)$
$R(8, 4)$	$R'(1, 6)$
$S(2, 4)$	$S'(-5, 6)$

Draw the image $P'Q'R'S'$.

Guidelines:

- The image of a translation is congruent to the original and has the same orientation as the original.
- The motion rule tells you how to translate each vertex of a figure in a coordinate plane.

EXERCISES

In Exercises 1–3, match the graph with the ordered pair that describes the translation.

a.

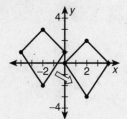

b.

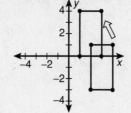

c.

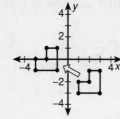

1. $(x - 1, y + 3)$ **2.** $(x + 4, y - 1)$ **3.** $(x - 4, y + 2)$

What you should learn:

11.6	How to recognize similar figures and how to use properties of similar figures

Correlation to Pupil's Textbook:

Chapter Test (p. 535)
Exercise 20

Examples	*Recognizing Similar Figures and Using Properties of Similar Figures*

a. Triangles RST and EFG at the right are similar. Name three pairs of corresponding angles that have the same measure. Then write three equal ratios for the similar triangles.

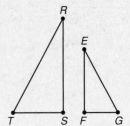

Two triangles are similar if their corresponding angles have the same measures. For similar triangles, the ratios of corresponding sides are equal.

Corresponding Angles

$m\angle R = m\angle E$

$m\angle T = m\angle G$

$m\angle S = m\angle F$

Corresponding Sides

$$\frac{RT}{EG} = \frac{RS}{EF} = \frac{ST}{FG}$$

b. In the figure at the right, $\triangle ABC \sim \triangle DEF$. Find FD and FE.

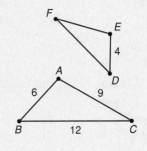

Because the triangles are similar, the ratios of the lengths of corresponding sides are equal. You can write proportions that allow you to solve for the missing lengths, FD and FE.

$$\frac{FD}{CA} = \frac{DE}{AB}$$

$$\frac{FD}{9} = \frac{4}{6}$$

$$9 \cdot \frac{FD}{9} = 9 \cdot \frac{4}{6}$$

$$FD = 6$$

$$\frac{FE}{CB} = \frac{DE}{AB}$$

$$\frac{FE}{12} = \frac{4}{6}$$

$$12 \cdot \frac{FE}{12} = 12 \cdot \frac{4}{6}$$

$$FE = 8$$

Guidelines:

- Similar figures have the same shape but not necessarily the same size.
- If two triangles are similar, the common ratio of corresponding sides is the scale factor of the one triangle to the other triangle.

EXERCISES

In Exercises 1–4, quadrilaterals $JKLM$ and $WXYZ$ are similar, as shown at the right.

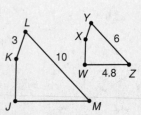

1. Name four pairs of angles that have the same measures.

2. Write four equal ratios for the quadrilaterals.

3. Find the scale factor of $WXYZ$ to $JKLM$.

4. Find XY and JM.

What you should learn:

11.7	How to use similar figures to solve real-life problems and how to compare perimeters and areas of similar figures

Correlation to Pupil's Textbook:

Chapter Test (p. 535)
Exercises 14, 15

Examples   *Using Similar Figures and Comparing Perimeters and Areas*

a. You are painting your school's mascot on the hallway floor of the school, using the sketch of the painting shown at the right. You want the actual painting to have a base of 6 feet. Find the lengths of the sides of the actual painting.

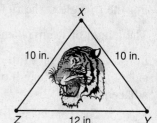

The angle measures of the actual painting are the same as the angle measures of the sketch. The actual painting has a base of 6 feet or 72 inches. Use a proportion to find the lengths of the sides of the painting.

Verbal Model
$$\frac{\text{Actual painting side}}{\text{Sketch side}} = \frac{\text{Actual painting base}}{\text{Sketch base}}$$

Labels
Side of actual painting $= x$ (inches)
Base of actual painting $= 72$ (inches)
Side of sketch $= 10$ (inches)
Base of sketch $= 12$ (inches)

Algebraic Model
$$\frac{x}{10} = \frac{72}{12}$$

$$10 \cdot \frac{x}{10} = 10 \cdot \frac{72}{12}$$

$$x = 60$$

The lengths of the sides of the actual painting should be 60 inches.

b. Compare the perimeter of the actual painting in Example a to the sketch.

The perimeters of the sketch and the painting are as follows.

Perimeter of sketch $= 10 + 12 + 10 = 32$ inches.

Perimeter of painting $= 60 + 72 + 60 = 192$ inches.

The ratio of the perimeter of the actual painting to the perimeter of the sketch is

$$\frac{\text{Perimeter of Actual Painting}}{\text{Perimeter of Sketch}} = \frac{192 \text{ inches}}{32 \text{ inches}} = \frac{6}{1}.$$

Guidelines: • When two figures are similar, remember that corresponding angles are congruent and corresponding sides are proportional.

EXERCISE

The height of the actual painting is 48 inches and the height of the sketch is 8 inches. Compare the area of the actual painting in Example a to the area of the sketch.

Reteach
Chapter 11

Name _____

What you should learn:

11.8	How to find trigonometric ratios and how to use the Pythagorean Theorem to find trigonometric ratios

Correlation to Pupil's Textbook:

Chapter Test (p. 535)
Exercises 16, 18

Examples	*Finding Trigonometric Ratios and Using the Pythagorean Theorem*

a. For the triangle at the right, find the sine, cosine, and tangent of $\angle A$ and $\angle C$.

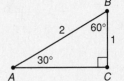

The length of the hypotenuse is 13.

For $\angle A$, the length of the opposite side is 5, and the length of the adjacent side is 12.

For $\angle C$, the length of the opposite side is 12, and the length of the adjacent side is 5.

$$\sin A = \frac{\text{Side opposite } \angle A}{\text{Hypotenuse}} = \frac{5}{13}$$

$$\cos A = \frac{\text{Side adjacent to } \angle A}{\text{Hypotenuse}} = \frac{12}{13}$$

$$\tan A = \frac{\text{Side opposite } \angle A}{\text{Side adjacent to } \angle A} = \frac{5}{12}$$

$$\sin C = \frac{\text{Side opposite } \angle C}{\text{Hypotenuse}} = \frac{12}{13}$$

$$\cos C = \frac{\text{Side adjacent to } \angle C}{\text{Hypotenuse}} = \frac{5}{13}$$

$$\tan C = \frac{\text{Side opposite } \angle C}{\text{Side adjacent to } \angle C} = \frac{12}{5}$$

b. In the triangle at the right, the length of the hypotenuse is twice the length of the shortest side. Use the Pythagorean Theorem to find the length of the third side. Then use the triangle to find the sine, cosine, and tangent of $\angle A$.

$$c^2 = a^2 + b^2 \qquad \textit{Pythagorean Theorem}$$

$$2^2 = 1^2 + b^2 \qquad \textit{Substitute for c and a.}$$

$$4 = 1 + b^2 \qquad \textit{Simplify.}$$

$$3 = b^2 \qquad \textit{Subtract 1 from each side.}$$

$$\sqrt{3} = b \qquad \textit{Square Root Principle}$$

Use $a = 1$, $b = \sqrt{3}$, and $c = 2$ to find the sine, cosine, and tangent of $\angle A$.

$$\sin 30° = \frac{\text{opp.}}{\text{hyp.}} = \frac{1}{2} \qquad \cos 30° = \frac{\text{adj.}}{\text{hyp.}} = \frac{\sqrt{3}}{2} \approx 0.87 \qquad \tan 30° = \frac{\text{opp.}}{\text{adj.}} = \frac{1}{\sqrt{3}} \approx 0.58$$

Guidelines: • A trigonometric ratio is a ratio of the length of two sides of a right triangle. (It depends only on the angle measure.)

EXERCISES

In Exercises 1–6, use $\triangle RST$ at the right to find the trigonometric ratio. **Round your results to two decimal places.**

1. $\sin R$

2. $\cos R$

3. $\cos S$

4. $\tan S$

5. $\sin S$

6. $\tan R$

7. Find the sine, cosine, and tangent of $\angle B$ in Example b above.

Name _____

What you should learn:

| 11.9 | How to use trigonometric ratios to solve right triangles and how to use trigonometric ratios to solve real-life problems |

Correlation to Pupil's Textbook:

Chapter Test (p. 535)
Exercises 12, 13, 17, 19

Example | *Solving Right Triangles and Solving Real-Life Problems*

a. You are designing a ramp for performing tricks on water skis. If the length of the ramp is 12 feet, what is the length of the vertical drop, d?

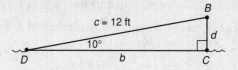

To find d, you can write the trigonometric ratio for the sine of $\angle D$.

$$\sin D = \frac{d}{c} \qquad \textit{Definition of sine of D}$$

$$\sin 10° = \frac{d}{12} \qquad \textit{Substitute for D and c.}$$

$$0.1736 \approx \frac{d}{12} \qquad \textit{Use a calculator.}$$

$$12(0.1736) \approx \frac{12d}{12} \qquad \textit{Multiply each side by 12.}$$

$$2.08 \approx d \qquad \textit{Simplify.}$$

The length of the vertical drop, d, is about 2.08 feet.

Guidelines:
- You can use a trigonometric ratio to solve a right triangle when you are given the length of one of the sides and the measure of one of the acute angles.

EXERCISES

In Exercises 1–4, find x. Round your results to two decimal places.

1.
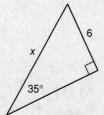

2.
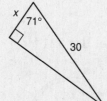

3.
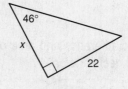

4.
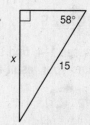

5. If you change your ramp design in Example a so that the ramp is elevated 25° from the water, what is the length of the vertical drop, d?

Name _____

What you should learn:

| 12.1 | How to find the circumference of a circle and how to find the area of a circle |

Correlation to Pupil's Textbook:

Mid-Chapter Self-Test (p. 558)   **Chapter Test (p. 581)**
Exercises 1–4, 18–20   Exercises 4, 5

| **Examples** | *The Circumference of a Circle and Finding the Area of a Circle* |

a. Find the circumference of the compact disc at the right.

Let d be the diameter of a circle and r be its radius. The circumference, C, of the circle is

$$C = \pi d \text{ or } C = 2\pi r.$$

Because the compact disc has a radius of 6 centimeters, it follows that its circumference is

$C = 2\pi r$ *Formula for circumference*

$\approx 2(3.14)(6)$ *Substitute for π and r.*

≈ 37.7 *Simplify.*

The circumference of the compact disc is about 37.7 centimeters.

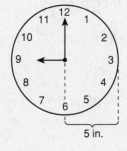
6 cm

b. Find the area of the clock face at the right.

Let r be the radius of a circle. The area, A, of the circle is $A = \pi r^2$.

Because the radius of the clock is 5 inches, it follows that its area is

$A = \pi r^2$ *Formula for area of a circle*

$\approx (3.14)(5)^2$ *Substitute for π and r.*

≈ 78.5 *Simplify.*

The area of the clock face is about 78.5 square inches.

5 in.

Guidelines:

- The diameter of a circle is the distance across the circle through its center.
- The radius of a circle is the distance from the center to any point on the circle.
- The circumference of a circle is the distance around the circle.

EXERCISES

In Exercises 1–4, find the circumference and area of the figure. Use 3.14 for π. Round your result to one decimal place.

1.

$d = 1.8$ cm

2.

$r = 16$ cm

3.

$r = 4.5$ in.

4.

$d = 2.5$ in.

Reteach
Chapter 12

Name _____

What you should learn:

12.2	How to identify parts of a polyhedron and how to identify parts of cones, cylinders, and spheres

Correlation to Pupil's Textbook:

Mid-Chapter Self-Test (p. 558) Chapter Test (p. 581)
Exercises 5–9   Exercises 1–3

Examples | *Identifying Parts of Polyhedrons and Identifying Parts of Other Solids*

a. Match the parts of a polyhedron with the correct description.

1. faces
2. vertices
3. edges
4. polyhedron

a. a solid that is bounded by polygons
b. segments where the faces meet
c. polygons that bound a polyhedron
d. points where the edges meet

Answers: 1. c 2. d 3. b 4. a

b. Name each solid below. Then identify the parts of each solid.

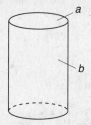   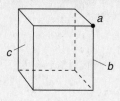   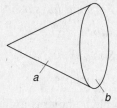

The solid is a cylinder.
a. base
b. lateral surface

The polyhedron is a prism.
a. vertex
b. edge
c. face

The solid is a cone.
a. lateral surface
b. base

Guidelines:

- Two common types of polyhedrons are prisms and pyramids.
- Three other types of common solids are spheres, cylinders, and cones.
- A net is a pattern that can be folded to form a solid.

EXERCISES

In Exercises 1–4, identify the parts of the solid.

1.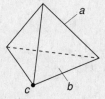

2.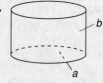

3.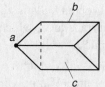

4.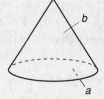

5. Name the solid that results from folding the net below.

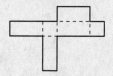

What you should learn:

12.3	How to find the surface area of a prism and a cylinder and how to use surface area to answer questions about real-life

Correlation to Pupil's Textbook:

Mid-Chapter Self-Test (p. 558)   Chapter Test (p. 581)
Exercises 10–13   Exercises 6, 10, 11,
                                                                    12, 15, 17

Examples   *Finding Surface Area and Solving Real-Life Problems*

a. Find the surface area of the prism at the right.

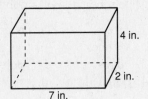

The surface area of a prism is $S = 2B + Ph$, where B is the area of a base, P is the perimeter of a base, and h is the height of the prism.

Each rectangular base has a width of 2 inches and a length of 7 inches. This means that each base has a surface area of $B = l \cdot w$ or 14 square inches. The perimeter of each base is $P = 2l + 2w$ or $2(7) + 2(2) = 18$ inches. The height is $h = 4$ inches. The surface area is:

$$S = 2B + Ph \qquad \textit{Formula for surface area of prism}$$
$$= 2(14) + (18)(4) \qquad \textit{Substitute for B, P, and h.}$$
$$= 100 \qquad \textit{Simplify.}$$

The surface area is 100 square inches.

b. Suppose the prism in Example a above is a gift box that you are wrapping with paper. You are also wrapping a cylindrical can of tennis balls. The can has a radius of 1.5 inches and a height of 9 inches. Which gift uses less paper?

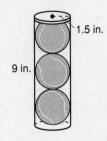

The surface area of a cylinder is $S = 2B + Ch$, where B is the area of a base, C is the circumference of a base, and h is the height of the cylinder. The area of each base is $B = \pi r^2$ or 2.25π square inches. The circumference of each base is $C = 2(1.5)\pi$ or 3π inches. The height is 9 inches. The surface area of the can of balls is:

$$S = 2B + Ch \qquad \textit{Formula for surface area of cylinder}$$
$$= 2(2.25\pi) + (3\pi)(9) \qquad \textit{Substitute for B, C, and h.}$$
$$= 31.5\pi \qquad \textit{Simplify.}$$
$$\approx 98.9 \qquad \textit{Use a calculator.}$$

The surface area of the can of tennis balls is about 98.9 square inches. The cylindrical gift has less surface area, which means that it uses less paper than the prism in Example a.

Guidelines:

- The surface area of a polyhedron is the sum of the areas of its faces.

EXERCISES

1. Find the surface area of a cube with a side of length 4 inches.

2. Find the surface area of a cylinder with a radius of 5 cm and a height of 8 cm.

Name _____

What you should learn:

12.4	How to find the volume of a prism and how to use the volume of a prism to solve real-life problems

Correlation to Pupil's Textbook:

Mid-Chapter Self-Test (p. 558)   **Chapter Test (p. 581)**
Exercises 14–17   Exercises 9, 13, 16

Examples   *Finding the Volume of a Prism and Solving Real-Life Problems*

a. Find the volume of the prism at the right.

The volume of a prism is $V = Bh$ where B is the area of a base and h is the height of the prism.

Each base is a right triangle. This means that each base has an area $B = \frac{1}{2}b \cdot h = \frac{1}{2}(6)(8) = 24$ square centimeters. The height of the prism is 3 centimeters. The volume is

$V = Bh$	*Formula for volume of prism*
$= (24)(3)$	*Substitute for B and h.*
$= 72$	*Simplify.*

The volume of the prism is 72 cubic centimeters.

b. You are buying a new refrigerator. It must fit into an opening that is 36 inches long, 66 inches high, and 30 inches wide. Find the volume, in cubic feet, of the opening for the refrigerator.

The volume of a rectangular prism (a prism whose sides are all rectangles) is $V = lwh$, where l is the length, w is the width, and h is the height of the prism.

The opening is a rectangular prism with a width of 30 inches or 2.5 feet. Its length is 36 inches or 3 feet and its height is 66 inches or 5.5 feet. The volume of the rectangular prism is

$V = l \cdot w \cdot h$	*Formula for volume of rectangular prism*
$= (3)(2.5)(5.5)$	*Substitute for l, w, and h.*
$= 41.25$	*Simplify.*

The volume of the opening for the refrigerator is 41.25 cubic feet.

Guidelines: • The standard measures of volume are cubic units such as cubic inches, cubic centimeters, and cubic feet.

EXERCISES

In Exercises 1–4, find the volume of the prism.

1.
5 in.
$B = 24$ in.^{2}

2.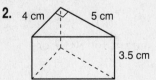
4 cm   5 cm
3.5 cm

3.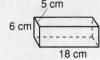
5 cm
6 cm
18 cm

4.
9 ft
$B = 7.8$ ft^2

Reteach
Chapter 12

Name _____

What you should learn:

12.5	How to find the volume of a cylinder and how to use the volume of a cylinder to solve real-life problems

Correlation to Pupil's Textbook:

Chapter Test (p. 581)
Exercises 7, 18, 19

Examples | *Finding the Volume of a Cylinder and Solving Real-Life Problems*

a. Find the volume of the cylinder at the right.

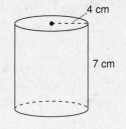

You can find the volume of a cylinder using $V = Bh$ where B is the area of a base and h is the height. The area of the base of this cylinder is $\pi(4)^2$ or about 50.24 square centimeters. The volume of the cylinder is

$$V = Bh \qquad \textit{Volume of cylinder}$$
$$\approx (50.24)(7) \qquad \textit{Substitute for B and h.}$$
$$\approx 351.68. \qquad \textit{Simplify.}$$

The volume is about 351.68 cubic centimeters.

b. Find the volume of the cylinder at the right. Compare your result with the result in Example a.

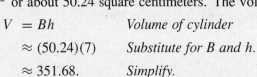

The area of the base of this cylinder is $\pi(7)^2$ or about 153.86 square centimeters. The volume of the cylinder is

$$V = Bh \qquad \textit{Volume of cylinder}$$
$$\approx (153.86)(4) \qquad \textit{Substitute for B and h.}$$
$$\approx 615.44. \qquad \textit{Simplify.}$$

The volume is about 615.44 cubic centimeters. When you interchange the radius of the base and the height of a cylinder as is done in these examples, you change its volume.

Guidelines:
- The volume of a cylinder is the product of its height and the area of its base.
- Liters, gallons, quarts, and fluid ounces are commonly used units for volume.

EXERCISES

In Exercises 1–4, find the volume of the cylinder. Use 3.14 **for** π.

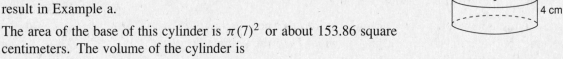

1. 3 in. / 3 in. **2.** 2 ft / 4 ft **3.** 5 cm / 1 cm **4.** 1 in. / 3.5 in.

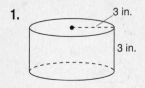 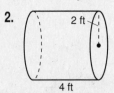 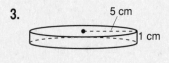 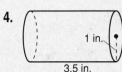

5. You are shopping for oil for your car. You can buy a quart for $0.97 or you can buy a liter for $1.09. Which is the better buy? (Hint: 1 liter = 33.8 fluid ounces)

What you should learn:

<table>
<tr><td>**12.6**</td><td>How to find the volume of a pyramid and a cone and how to use the volume of a pyramid and a cone to solve real-life problems</td></tr>
</table>

Correlation to Pupil's Textbook:

Chapter Test (p. 581)

Exercise 8

Examples | *Volumes of Pyramids and Cones and Solving Real-Life Problems*

a. Find the volume of the pyramid at the right.

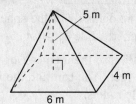

You can find the volume of a pyramid using $V = \frac{1}{3}Bh$, where B is the area of a base and h is the height of the pyramid.

The base of the pyramid is a rectangle with an area of $6 \cdot 4$ or 24 square meters. Because the height of the pyramid is 5 meters, it follows that the volume of the pyramid is

$V = \frac{1}{3}Bh$ *Volume of a pyramid*

$= \frac{1}{3}(24)(5)$ *Substitute for B and h.*

$= 40$ *Simplify.*

The pyramid has a volume of 40 cubic meters.

b. Find the volume of the cone-shaped pile of sand at the right. Use 3.14 for π.

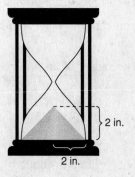

You can find the volume of a cone using $V = \frac{1}{3}Bh$, where B is the area of a base and h is the height of the cone.

Because the height of the cone is 2 inches, it follows that the volume is

$V = \frac{1}{3}Bh$ *Volume of a cone*

$= \frac{1}{3}(\pi r^2)(h)$ *Area of base is πr^2.*

$= \frac{1}{3}(\pi 2^2)(2)$ *Substitute for r and h.*

$= \frac{8\pi}{3}$ *Simplify.*

≈ 8.37 *Use a calculator.*

The volume of the pile of sand is about 8.37 cubic inches.

Guidelines: • The volume of a pyramid or cone is one-third the product of its height and the area of its base.

EXERCISES

In Exercises 1–4, find the volume of the solid. Use 3.14 for π.

1.

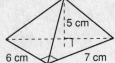

5 cm

6 cm   7 cm

2.

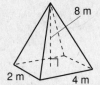

8 m

2 m   4 m

3.

12 in.

5 in.

4.

9 ft

11 ft

What you should learn:

12.7	How to find the volume of a sphere and how to use the volume of a sphere to solve real-life problems

Correlation to Pupil's Textbook:

Chapter Test (p. 581)
Exercise 20

Examples | *Finding Volumes of Spheres and Solving Real-Life Problems*

a. The diameter of the sphere at the right is 18 feet. Find the volume of the sphere. Use 3.14 for π.

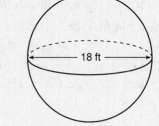

18 ft

Because the diameter of the sphere is 18 feet, you know that the radius is 9 feet. You can find the volume of a sphere using $V = \frac{4}{3}\pi r^3$, where r is the radius.

$V = \frac{4}{3}\pi r^3$ *Volume of a sphere*

$= \frac{4}{3}\pi(9)^3$ *Substitute for r.*

≈ 3052.08 *Use a calculator.*

The volume of the sphere is about 3052.08 cubic feet.

b. The radius of an orange is 1.5 inches. Find the volume of the orange.

You can find the volume of a sphere using $V = \frac{4}{3}\pi r^3$, where r is the radius.

The radius of an orange is 1.5 inches, therefore, its volume is

$V = \frac{4}{3}\pi r^3$ *Volume of a sphere*

$= \frac{4}{3}\pi(1.5)^3$ *Substitute for r.*

≈ 14.13 *Use a calculator.*

The volume is about 14.13 cubic inches.

$r = 1.5$ in.

Guidelines: • The volume of a sphere is four-thirds times π times the cube of its radius.

EXERCISES

In Exercises 1–4, find the volume of the sphere. Use 3.14 for π. Round your results to two decimal places.

1. $r = 3.6$ in.   **2.** $d = 16$ in.   **3.** $d = 28$ cm   **4.** $r = 3.25$ in.

3.6 in.

16 in.

28 cm

3.25 in.

5. Find the radius of a sphere with a volume of 682.67π cm^3.

Reteach
Chapter 12

Name _____

Correlation to Pupil's Textbook:

Chapter Test (p. 581)

Exercise 14

What you should learn:

12.8	Explore ratios of measurements of similar figures and how to use ratios of measurements of similar figures

---

Examples *Exploring Measures of Similar Solids and Comparing Ratios of Similar Solids*

a. Match the solid at the right with a similar solid shown below.

1.   2. 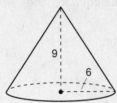   3.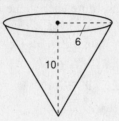

The solid at the right is similar to solid number 2, because they have the same shape and their corresponding lengths are proportional.

b. The similar pyramids at the right have a scale factor of $\frac{3}{2}$.

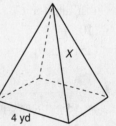

1. Find the ratio of the surface area of Pyramid X to the surface area of Pyramid Y.

2. Find the ratio of the volume of Pyramid X to the volume of Pyramid Y.

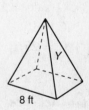

1. If two solids are similar with a scale factor of $\frac{3}{2}$, then the ratio of the surface area of the larger solid, Pyramid X, to the surface area of the smaller solid, Pyramid Y, is $\left(\frac{3}{2}\right)^2$, or $\frac{9}{4}$.

2. If two solids are similar with a scale factor of $\frac{3}{2}$, then the ratio of the volume of the larger solid, Pyramid X, to the volume of the smaller solid, Pyramid Y, is $\left(\frac{3}{2}\right)^3$, or $\frac{27}{8}$.

Guidelines:
- Two solids are similar if they have the same shape and their corresponding lengths are proportional.

EXERCISES

In Exercises 1–3, use the similar cylinders at the right. Use 3.14 for π.

1. Find the scale factor of Cylinder A to Cylinder B.

2. Find the surface area of Cylinder A.

3. Use the ratio of measures of similar solids to find the surface area of Cylinder B.

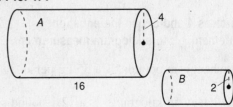

Name _____

What you should learn:

13.1	How to find solutions of a linear equation in two variables and how to organize solutions of real-life problems using linear equations

Correlation to Pupil's Textbook:

Mid-Chapter Self-Test (p. 608)   Chapter Test (p. 631)

Exercises 1–6   Exercises 1, 5–7

Examples   *Solutions of Linear Equations and Solving Real-Life Problems*

a. List three solutions of $3x + 2y = 12$.

8 Choose three values of x. Substitute each value into the equation and solve the resulting equation for y.

x-value	Substitute for x.	Solve for y.	Solution
$x = 0$	$3(0) + 2y = 12$	$y = 6$	$(0, 6)$
$x = 2$	$3(2) + 2y = 12$	$y = 3$	$(2, 3)$
$x = 4$	$3(4) + 2y = 12$	$y = 0$	$(4, 0)$

b. Find the Fahrenheit temperature, F, that corresponds to the Celsius temperatures $10°$ and $25°$. Use the linear equation $F = \frac{9}{5}C + 32$.

C-value	Substitute for C.	Solve for F.	Solution
$C = 10$	$\frac{9}{5}(10) + 32$	$F = 50$	$(10, 50)$
$C = 25$	$\frac{9}{5}(25) + 32$	$F = 77$	$(25, 77)$

Guidelines:

- In a linear equation, variables occur to the first power.
- Most equations involving two variables have many solutions.
- To find solutions of linear equations in two variables, choose a value for one of the variables, substitute that value into the equation, and then solve for the other variable.

EXERCISES

In Exercises 1–3, find several solutions of the linear equation. Use a table of values to organize your results.

1. $x + 5y = 20$ **2.** $2x - y = 6$ **3.** $3x - 2y = 18$

In Exercises 4 and 5, use the equation $y = 2.2x$ which relates a pound measurement, y, to a kilogram measurement, x.

4. How heavy, in pounds, is a 55 kg person?

5. How heavy, in kilograms, is a 12.1 pound shipping carton?

Reteach
Chapter 13

Name _____

What you should learn:

13.2 How to use a table of values to sketch the graph of a linear equation and how to recognize graphs of horizontal and vertical lines

Correlation to Pupil's Textbook:

Mid-Chapter Self-Test (p. 608)
Exercises 7, 8

Examples | Graphing Linear Equations and Horizontal and Vertical Lines

a. Sketch the graph of $y = 3x + 1$.

Begin by making a table of values.

x Value	Substitute	Solve for y	Solution
$x = -2$	$y = 3(-2) + 1$	$y = -5$	$(-2, -5)$
$x = -1$	$y = 3(-1) + 1$	$y = -2$	$(-1, -2)$
$x = 0$	$y = 3(0) + 1$	$y = 1$	$(0, 1)$
$x = 1$	$y = 3(1) + 1$	$y = 4$	$(1, 4)$

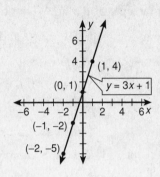

Plot the solutions in a coordinate plane. Then draw a line through the points. The line at the right is the graph of the equation.

b. Sketch the graph of $x = 2$.

The graph of the equation $x = a$ is a vertical line that passes through the point $(a, 0)$. When $x = 2$, the graph is a vertical line that passes through the point $(2, 0)$.

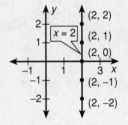

c. Sketch the graph of $y = -1$.

The graph of the equation $y = b$ is a horizontal line that passes through the point $(0, b)$. When $y = -1$, the graph is a horizontal line that passes through the point $(0, -1)$.

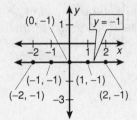

Guidelines:

- The graph of an equation is the graph of all of its solutions.
- The graph of every linear equation is a line.
- The graph of a linear equation in only one variable is either a vertical line or a horizontal line.

EXERCISES

In Exercises 1–3, decide whether the ordered pair is a solution to the equation. If not, find a solution.

1. $(-1, 4)$; $3x + y = 7$

2. $(5, 2)$; $x = 2$

3. $(3, 2)$; $y = \frac{1}{3}x + 1$

In Exercises 4–6, sketch the graph of the equation.

4. $y = 2x - 1$

5. $y = -4x + 2$

6. $y = 4$

What you should learn:

13.3	How to find intercepts of lines and how to use intercepts to sketch quick graphs

Correlation to Pupil's Textbook:

Mid-Chapter Self-Test (p. 608)   Chapter Test (p. 631)
Exercises 9–11, 17–20   Exercises 2, 3, 9

Examples   *Finding Intercepts of Lines and Sketching Quick Graphs*

a. Find the intercepts of the line given by $y = -3x + 9$.

To find the x-intercept, let $y = 0$ and solve for x.

$y = -3x + 9$	*Rewrite original equation.*
$0 = -3x + 9$	*Substitute 0 for y.*
$-9 = -3x$	*Subtract 9 from each side.*
$3 = x$	*Divide each side by −3.*

The x-intercept is 3. The graph contains the point (3, 0).

To find the y-intercept, let $x = 0$ and solve for y.

$y = -3x + 9$	*Rewrite original equation.*
$y = -3(0) + 9$	*Substitute 0 for x.*
$y = 9$	*Simplify.*

The y-intercept is 9. The graph contains the point (0, 9).

b. Sketch a quick graph of $y = -3x + 9$, the equation in Example a above.

Plot the two solutions (3, 0) and (0, 9) from Example a. These solutions are the intercepts of the graph of the line. Draw a line through the two plotted points.

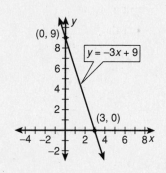

Guidelines: • An x-intercept of a graph is the x-coordinate of a point where the graph crosses the x-axis; a y-intercept of a graph is the y-coordinate of a point where the graph crosses the y-axis.

EXERCISES

In Exercises 1–4, find the intercepts of the line.

1. $x + y = 7$ **2.** $2x - y = 6$ **3.** $y = \frac{1}{2}x + 3$ **4.** $4x - 3y = 24$

In Exercises 5–7, sketch a line having the given intercepts.

5. x-intercept: 4
y-intercept: -2

6. x-intercept: -2
y-intercept: -3

7. x-intercept: 1
y-intercept: 5

Name _____

What you should learn:

13.4 How to find the slope of a line and how to interpret the slope of a line

Correlation to Pupil's Textbook:

Mid-Chapter Self-Test (p. 608) **Chapter Test (p. 631)**
Exercises 12–20   Exercises 4, 8, 10, 11

Examples *Finding the Slope of a Line and Interpreting Slope*

a. Find the slope of the line through $(1, 7)$ and $(3, 4)$.

The slope m of the nonvertical line passing through (x_1, y_1) and (x_2, y_2) is

$$m = \frac{y_2 - y_1}{x_2 - x_1} = \frac{\text{Rise}}{\text{Run}}.$$

Let $(1, 7)$ be (x_1, y_1) and let $(3, 4)$ be (x_2, y_2). Then

$$m = \frac{4 - 7}{3 - 1} = \frac{-3}{2}.$$

Because the slope is negative, the line falls to the right.

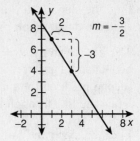

b. Compare the slopes of the lines through the indicated points.

Line 1: $(4, 6), (6, 10)$ Line 2: $(1, 1), (7, 0)$

Line 1: $m = \dfrac{10 - 6}{6 - 4} = \dfrac{4}{2} = 2$ Line 2: $m = \dfrac{0 - 1}{7 - 1} = \dfrac{-1}{6}$

The slope of line 1 is positive, and the slope of line 2 is negative. Line 1 is steeper than line 2, because its rise is greater than its run.

Guidelines:

- The slope of a line is the ratio of the change in y (called the "rise") to the change in x (called the "run").
- The slope of a line tells you whether the line rises to the right (positive slope), falls to the right (negative slope), or is horizontal (zero slope).
- The slope of a line also tells you how steep the line is.

EXERCISES

In Exercises 1–3, find the slope of the line.

1.

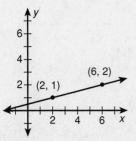

2.

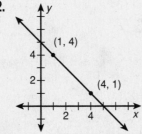

3.

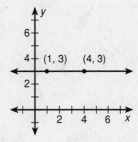

In Exercises 4–6, plot the points. Then find the slope of the line through the points.

4. $(0, 6), (4, 0)$ **5.** $(2, 4), (4, 8)$ **6.** $(-3, 5), (2, 5)$

What you should learn:

13.5	How to find the slope and y-intercept of a line from its equation and how to use the slope-intercept form to sketch a quick graph

Correlation to Pupil's Textbook:

Chapter Test (p. 631)

Exercises 9, 12, 13

Examples   *Using the Slope-Intercept Form and Sketching Quick Graphs*

a. Find the slope and y-intercept of the line given by $y = -2x + 3$. Then sketch a quick graph of the line.

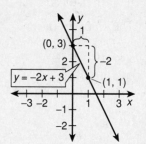

The line given by $y = -2x + 3$ is in the form $y = mx + b$. It has a slope of -2 and a y-intercept of 3. First plot the y-intercept, $(0, 3)$. Locate a second point on the line by moving 1 unit to the right and 2 units down. Draw the line through the two points.

b. Find the slope and y-intercept of the line given by $3x + 2y = 8$.

To use the slope-intercept form, you must write the linear equation in the form $y = mx + b$. You must solve the equation $3x + 2y = 8$ for y.

$3x + 2y = 8$ *Rewrite original equation.*

$2y = -3x + 8$ *Subtract $3x$ from each side.*

$y = -\frac{3}{2}x + 4$ *Divide each side by 2.*

The line given by $y = -\frac{3}{2}x + 4$ has a slope of $-\frac{3}{2}$ and a y-intercept of 4.

Guidelines:

- The linear equation $y = mx + b$ is in slope-intercept form. In this form, m is the slope and b is the y-intercept.

EXERCISES

In Exercises 1–3, match the equation with its graph.

a.
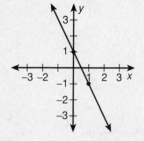

b.
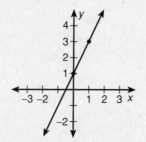

c.
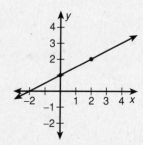

1. $y = 2x + 1$ **2.** $y = -2x + 1$ **3.** $y = \frac{1}{2}x + 1$

In Exercises 4–6, find the slope and y-intercept of the line. Then sketch a quick graph of the line.

4. $y = -\frac{4}{3}x - 2$ **5.** $4x - 8y = 0$ **6.** $7x - 14y = 21$

Name _____

What you should learn:

13.6	How to use graphs of linear equations to solve real-life problems and how to use scatter plots to create graphical models

Correlation to Pupil's Textbook:

Chapter Test (p. 631)

Exercises 19, 20

Examples *Using Graphs of Linear Equations and Using Scatter Plots*

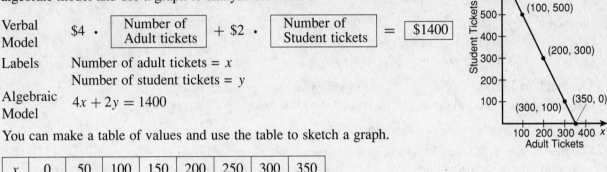

a. Your drama club is selling tickets for the spring musical. The club hopes to raise $1400 by charging $4 per adult and $2 per student. Write an algebraic model and use a graph to analyze the model.

Verbal Model $4 · [Number of Adult tickets] + $2 · [Number of Student tickets] = [$1400]

Labels   Number of adult tickets = x
Number of student tickets = y

Algebraic Model $4x + 2y = 1400$

You can make a table of values and use the table to sketch a graph.

x	0	50	100	150	200	250	300	350
y	700	600	500	400	300	200	100	0

b. The data in the table below shows the number of cruise passengers (in millions) from 1982 to 1990. Draw a scatter plot of the data.
(Cruise Lines International Association)

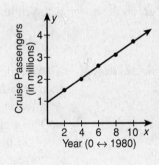

Year	1982	1984	1986	1988	1990
Cruise Passengers	1.5	2.0	2.6	3.1	3.7

Write the data as ordered pairs. Sketch a scatter plot, as shown at the right. Sketch the line that best fits the points.

Guidelines: • Two quantities that can be modeled with a linear equation are said to have a linear relationship.

EXERCISES

For Exercises 1–3, use the following: Your student government is selling school T-shirts, for $10 each, and sweatshirts, for $15 each. Your group wants to raise $1500.

1. Write a verbal and an algebraic model to represent the sales.

2. Make a table of values and graph the model.

3. Interpret the intercepts of the graph in a real-life context.

4. Use the line in Example b to estimate the number of cruise passengers (in millions) in 1992.

Reteach

Chapter 13

Name _____

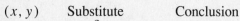

What you should learn:

13.7	How to check whether an ordered pair is a solution of a linear inequality and how to sketch the graph of a linear inequality

Correlation to Pupil's Textbook:

Chapter Test (p. 631)
Exercises 14, 15

Examples	*Solutions of Linear Inequalities and Graphing Linear Inequalities*

a. Check whether the ordered pairs $(0, -5)$, $(2, 2)$, and $(4, 3)$ are solutions of $y > 3x - 5$.

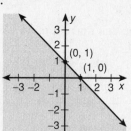

(x, y)	Substitute	Conclusion
$(0, -5)$	$-5 \overset{?}{>} 3(0) - 5$	$(0, -5)$ is not a solution.
$(2, 2)$	$2 \overset{?}{>} 3(2) - 5$	$(2, 2)$ is a solution.
$(4, 3)$	$3 \overset{?}{>} 3(4) - 5$	$(4, 3)$ is not a solution.

The graph of all solutions of $y > 3x - 5$ is shown at the right. The shaded region represents the solutions. Points on a dashed line are not solution points.

b. Sketch the graph of the linear inequality $y \leq -x + 1$.

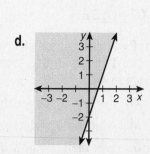

Use the intercepts $(0, 1)$ and $(1, 0)$ to graph the equation $y = -x + 1$ as a solid line. (For inequalities with $\leq$ or $\geq$ symbols, the points on the line are part of the graph.) Test several points above and below the line. Shade the side of the line which contains solutions of the inequality. The graph is shown at the right.

Guidelines:

- An ordered pair (x, y) is a solution of a linear inequality if the inequality is true when the values of x and y are substituted into the inequality.

- The graph of a linear inequality is a half-plane that consists of all points on one side of the line that is the graph of the corresponding linear equation.

- For the inequality symbols $>$ and $<$, the points on the line are not part of the graph (this is indicated by a dashed line).

EXERCISES

In Exercises 1–4, match the inequality with its graph. Then check if $(4, 0)$ **and** $(-2, 3)$ **are solutions.**

a.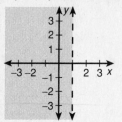

b.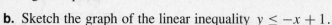

c.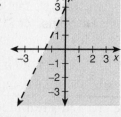

d.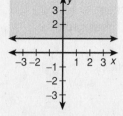

1. $y < 2x + 3$ **2.** $y \geq 3x - 2$ **3.** $x < 1$ **4.** $y \geq 1$

Name _____

What you should learn:

| 13.8 | How to find the distance between two points and how to find the midpoint between two points |

Correlation to Pupil's Textbook:

Chapter Test (p. 631)

Exercises 16–18

Examples | *Using the Distance Formula and Using the Midpoint Formula*

a. Find the distance between $(-5, 2)$ and $(3, -1)$.

The distance, d, between the points (x_1, y_1) and (x_2, y_2) is

$$d = \sqrt{(x_2 - x_1)^2 + (y_2 - y_1)^2}.$$

Let $(x_1, y_1) = (-5, 2)$ and $(x_2, y_2) = (3, -1)$.

$$d = \sqrt{(3 - (-5))^2 + (-1 - 2)^2}$$

$$= \sqrt{8^2 + (-3)^2}$$

$$= \sqrt{73}$$

$$\approx 8.54$$

The distance between the points is about 8.54 units.

b. Find the midpoint between $(-4, -5)$ and $(8, 3)$.

The midpoint between (x_1, y_1) and (x_2, y_2) is $\left(\dfrac{x_1 + x_2}{2}, \dfrac{y_1 + y_2}{2} \right)$.

Let $(x_1, y_1) = (-4, -5)$ and $(x_2, y_2) = (8, 3)$.

$$\text{Midpoint} = \left(\frac{-4 + 8}{2}, \frac{-5 + 3}{2} \right)$$

$$= (2, -1)$$

The coordinates of the midpoint are $(2, -1)$.

Guidelines: • You can obtain the Distance Formula by using the Pythagorean Theorem with two general points (x_1, y_1) and (x_2, y_2).

EXERCISES

In Exercises 1 and 2, use the graph to estimate the distance between the points. Then use the Distance Formula to check your estimate.

In Exercises 3 and 4, use the graph to estimate the midpoint between the two points. Then use the Midpoint Formula to check your estimate.

1. **2.**

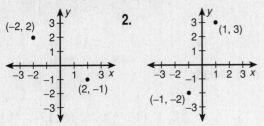

3. **4.**

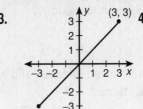
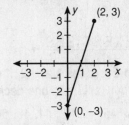

Reteach
Chapter 14

Name _____

What you should learn:

| 14.1 | How to find measures of central tendency and how to use measures of central tendency to solve real-life problems |

Correlation to Pupil's Textbook:

Mid-Chapter Self-Test (p. 652)
Exercises 1–3, 5, 6

Chapter Test (p. 678)
Exercises 5–7, 14

Examples | *Measures of Central Tendency and Using Measures of Central Tendenc*

a. Find the mean, median, and mode of the data
6, 9, 7, 6, 6, 7, 5, 9, 6, 6, 4, 7.

1. You can find the mean by finding the average of the numbers. Add the numbers and divide by 12.

$$\text{Mean} = \frac{6+9+7+6+6+7+5+9+6+6+4+7}{12} = 6.5$$

To find the median and the mode, you should first order the numbers from smallest to largest. In order, the numbers are 4, 5, 6, 6, 6, 6, 6, 7, 7, 7, 9, 9.

2. You can find the median by identifying the middle number (or average of the two middle numbers) when the numbers are listed in order. Because the two middle numbers of the data are 6 and 6, the median is 6.

3. You can find the mode of a group of numbers by finding the number that occurs most often. For this data, the mode is 6.

b. In your English class, you were asked to record the number of hours that you spend listening to music each day, for one week. Your data is given in the table below. Find the mean, median, and mode. Which measure of central tendency best describes the data?

Day	Sun	Mon	Tues	Wed	Thur	Fri	Sat
Hours	3	1.5	2	1	0	2.5	4

The data does not have a mode because there is no number that occurs more than once. The median of the data is 2, which occurs as the middle number. The measure of central tendency that best describes this data is the mean, or the average. The mean of this data is 2. You could say that you average 2 hours each day listening to music.

Guidelines:

• A measure of central tendency is a number that can be used to represent a group of numbers.

• The most common measures of central tendency are the mean, median, and mode.

EXERCISES

In Exercises 1 and 2, find the mean, median, and mode of the data. Round your results to one decimal place.

1. 45, 42, 42, 44, 48, 50

2. 12, 15, 16, 11, 12, 12, 14, 17, 16, 15, 17

110 *Chapter 14 ▪ Exploring Data and Polynomials*

Name _____

What you should learn:

14.2	How to organize data with a stem-and-leaf plot and how to use two stem-and-leaf plots to compare two sets of data

Correlation to Pupil's Textbook:

Mid-Chapter Self-Test (p. 652)   **Chapter Test (p. 678)**
Exercise 4   Exercises 14–16

Examples — *Using Stem-and-Leaf Plots and Using Double Stem-and-Leaf Plots*

a. Use a stem-and-leaf plot to order the following set of data.

Unordered Data: 6, 19, 23, 35, 15, 4, 26, 13, 7, 12, 3, 17, 22, 32, 10, 26, 18, 8, 27, 2, 15, 36, 13, 21, 30, 20, 5

You can let the stem represent the tens digit and let the leaves represent the units digit. Begin by creating an unordered stem-and- leaf plot as shown below at the left. Then order each leaf to form an ordered stem-and-leaf plot shown below at the right.

Unordered Plot		Ordered Plot	
Stem	Leaves	Stem	Leaves
3	5 2 6 0	3	0 2 5 6
2	3 6 2 6 7 1 0	2	0 1 2 3 6 6 7
1	9 5 3 2 7 0 8 5 3	1	0 2 3 3 5 5 7 8 9
0	6 4 7 3 8 2 5	0	2 3 4 5 6 7 8

3 | 5 represents 35   1 | 0 represents 10

You can use the ordered plot to order the data.

Ordered Data: 2, 3, 4, 5, 6, 7, 8, 10, 12, 13, 13, 15, 15, 17, 18, 19, 20, 21, 22, 23, 26, 26, 27, 30, 32, 35, 36

b. List the data represented by the double stem-and-leaf plot.

9 6 4	5	1 7 8 9
3 0	4	0 2 4 5
8 5 3 2	3	1 6

3 | 4 | 0 represents 43 and 40.

The ordered data on the left: 32, 33, 35, 38, 40, 43, 54, 56, 59

The ordered data on the right: 31, 36, 40, 42, 44, 45, 51, 57, 58, 59

Guidelines: • When you make a stem-and-leaf plot, you should include a key to tell what the stem and leaves represent.

EXERCISES

1. Use a stem-and-leaf plot to order the data: 24, 13, 17, 29, 11, 33, 20, 18, 39, 23, 10, 22, 28, 36, 22, 35, 15, 28, 37, 30, 26, 28, 19, 25, 12, 26

2. List the two sets of data represented by the double stem-and-leaf plot.

21	3	46
7551	2	79
32	0	258

1 | 3 | 4 represents 31 and 34.

What you should learn:

14.3	How to organize data with a box-and-whisker plot and how to use box-and-whisker plots to interpret real-life data

Correlation to Pupil's Textbook:

Mid-Chapter Self-Test (p. 652)   **Chapter Test (p. 678)**
Exercises 7–15   Exercises 1–4, 15, 16

Examples	*Drawing Box-and-Whisker Plots and Using Box-and-Whisker Plots*

a. Draw a box-and-whisker plot for the following data.

   36, 19, 24, 40, 16, 32, 45, 28, 37, 31, 30, 43, 17

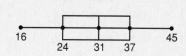

Write the numbers in increasing order and label five numbers: the smallest number, the quartiles, and the largest number. The median (or the second quartile) divides the collection of numbers into two halves. The first quartile is the median of the lower half, and the third quartile is the median of the upper half.

   16, 17, 19, 24, 28, 30, 31, 32, 36, 37, 40, 43, 45

From this ordering, you can see that the first quartile is 24, the second quartile is 31, and the third quartile is 37. The box-and-whisker plot for the data is shown at the right.

b. The data below lists the top 10 N.F.L. all-time leading touchdown scorers through 1992. Construct a box-and-whisker plot for the number of touchdowns (Source: National Football League, 1992).

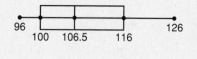

Scorer	TD's	Scorer	TD's
Jim Brown	126	Don Hutson	105
Walter Payton	125	Steve Largent	101
John Riggins	116	Franco Harris	100
Lenny Moore	113	Marcus Allen	98
Jerry Rice	108	Eric Dickerson	96

The first quartile is 100, the second quartile is 106.5, and the third quartile is 116. The box-and-whisker plot is shown at the right.

Guidelines:

- When you draw a box-and-whisker plot, you should space the quartiles, the smallest number, and the largest number as they would be on a number line.

EXERCISES

1. Name the smallest and largest numbers and name the quartiles for the box-and-whisker plot at the right which represent the ages of the teachers at a high school. What does the plot tell you about their ages?

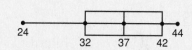

2. Draw a box-and-whisker plot for the data: 5, 12, 9, 13, 8, 17, 11, 3, 10, 19, 15, 4, 18

Reteach
Chapter 14

Name _____

What you should learn:

14.4	How to organize data with a matrix and how to add two matrices

Examples   *Using Matrices and Adding and Subtracting Matrices*

a. Your school's record of wins, losses, and ties for home and away basketball games is shown in the table at the right. Write this table as a matrix. Did the team have an overall winning record?

	Wins	Losses	Ties
Home	6	4	1
Away	3	7	0

The matrix associated with the table has two rows and three columns, as shown at the right. The team had 9 wins, 11 losses, and 1 tie. The team did not have an overall winning record.

$$\begin{matrix} & \text{Wins} & \text{Losses} & \text{Ties} \\ \text{Home} & & & \\ \text{Away} & & & \end{matrix} \begin{bmatrix} 6 & 4 & 1 \\ 3 & 7 & 0 \end{bmatrix}$$

b. Add and subtract the following matrices.

To add or subtract matrices, you simply add or subtract corresponding entries.

$$\begin{bmatrix} -6 & 4 \\ 2 & -1 \end{bmatrix} + \begin{bmatrix} 3 & -2 \\ 5 & -3 \end{bmatrix} = \begin{bmatrix} -6+3 & 4+(-2) \\ 2+5 & -1+(-3) \end{bmatrix} = \begin{bmatrix} -3 & 2 \\ 7 & -4 \end{bmatrix}$$

$$\begin{bmatrix} -6 & 4 \\ 2 & -1 \end{bmatrix} - \begin{bmatrix} 3 & -2 \\ 5 & -3 \end{bmatrix} = \begin{bmatrix} -6-3 & 4-(-2) \\ 2-5 & -1-(-3) \end{bmatrix} = \begin{bmatrix} -9 & 6 \\ -3 & 2 \end{bmatrix}$$

Guidelines:

- A matrix is a rectangular arrangement of numbers into rows and columns.
- The numbers in a matrix are called entries.
- Two matrices are equal if all of the entries in corresponding positions are equal.
- You cannot add or subtract matrices that are different sizes.

EXERCISES

In Exercises 1 and 2, find the sum and difference of the matrices.

1. $\begin{bmatrix} 7 & -1 \\ 12 & 4 \end{bmatrix}, \begin{bmatrix} 0 & 3 \\ -8 & -9 \end{bmatrix}$

2. $\begin{bmatrix} -5 & -7 & 4 \\ 10 & 2 & -14 \end{bmatrix}, \begin{bmatrix} 3 & 0 & -6 \\ 7 & -1 & 5 \end{bmatrix}$

3. Write the table shown below as a matrix.

	Sale price	Regular price
Shirts	13.00	18.50
Jeans	21.00	29.00
Belts	8.50	12.00

What you should learn:

14.5	How to identify polynomials and write them in standard form and how to use polynomials to solve real-life problems

Correlation to Pupil's Textbook:

Chapter Test (p. 678)
Exercises 10, 11

Examples	*Identifying Polynomials and Using Polynomials in Real Life*

a. Identify the number of terms in each polynomial and give its type.

Polynomial	Terms	Type
$16x^2 - 3x + 7$	3	Trinomial
$6y + 8$	2	Binomial
$25t^4$	1	Monomial

b. Simplify the polynomial $7s^2 + 8s - s^2 + 3s$. Then write the result in standard form.

To simplify a polynomial, combine like terms (two terms that have the same variable, raised to the same power). A polynomial is written in standard form if the powers of the variable decrease from left to right.

$$7s^2 + 8s - s^2 + 3s = 7s^2 - s^2 + 8s + 3s \qquad \textit{Standard form}$$

$$= (7 - 1)s^2 + (8 + 3)s \qquad \textit{Combine like terms.}$$

$$= 6s^2 + 11s \qquad \textit{Simplify.}$$

c. The height h (in feet) of an object after t seconds is given by

$$h = -16t^2 + 64.$$

Find the height when $t = 0$ seconds, 1 second, and 2 seconds.

To find the height, substitute the values of t into the given polynomial.

Time	Substitute	Height
$t = 0$ seconds	$h = -16(0)^2 + 64$	64 feet
$t = 1$ second	$h = -16(1)^2 + 64$	48 feet
$t = 2$ seconds	$h = -16(2)^2 + 64$	0 feet

Guidelines:

- A polynomial is an expression that has one or more terms of the form ax^n where the coefficient a is any real number and the exponent n is a whole number.

- The terms of a polynomial are considered to include any minus signs in the polynomial.

EXERCISES

In Exercises 1–3, simplify the polynomial and write the result in standard form. Then identify the type of polynomial for each result.

1. $6x + 5x^2 - 2x + 3$ **2.** $12 - w^2 + 3 + 5w^2$ **3.** $4y^2 - y + y^2 - 3y$

What you should learn:

14.6	How to add polynomials and how to subtract polynomials

Correlation to Pupil's Textbook:

Chapter Test (p. 678)
Exercises 12, 13

Examples	*Adding Polynomials and Subtracting Polynomials*

a. Use a horizontal format to add the polynomials $12p^3 - 5p^2 - 3p + 2$ and $4p^3 + 9p - 6$.

You can add two polynomials by combining like terms.

$$(12p^3 - 5p^2 - 3p + 2) + (4p^3 + 9p - 6) = 12p^3 - 5p^2 - 3p + 2 + 4p^3 + 9p - 6$$
$$= 12p^3 + 4p^3 - 5p^2 - 3p + 9p + 2 - 6$$
$$= 16p^3 - 5p^2 + 6p - 4$$

b. Use a horizontal format to subtract $-2a^2 + a - 6$ from $a^2 + a + 3$.

To subtract two polynomials, you can use the Distributive Property.

$$(a^2 + a + 3) - (-2a^2 + a - 6) = a^2 + a + 3 + 2a^2 - a + 6$$
$$= a^2 + 2a^2 + a - a + 3 + 6$$
$$= 3a^2 + 9$$

c. Use a vertical format to subtract $f^2 - 6f + 5$ from $8f^2 - 2f + 3$.

You must use two steps when you use the vertical format for subtraction.

Subtract

$$8f^2 - 2f + 3$$
$$\underline{-(\ f^2 - 6f + 5)}$$

Distribute

$$8f^2 - 2f + 3$$
$$\underline{-\ f^2 + 6f - 5}$$
$$7f^2 + 4f - 2$$

Guidelines:
- The degree of a polynomial is its largest exponent.
- Any two polynomials (with the same or different degrees) can be added or subtracted.
- When you use a vertical format to add or subtract two polynomials, be sure that you line up the like terms.

EXERCISES

1. Use a vertical format to add the polynomials.

$$8y^3 - 4y^2 + y - 9$$
$$\underline{-y^3 + 2y^2 - y + 5}$$

2. Use a vertical format to subtract the polynomials.

$$5m^4 + 3m^3 + m^2 - 2m + 7$$
$$\underline{-(-3m^4 + 8m^3 + m^2 + 3m - 2)}$$

In Exercises 3 and 4, perform the indicated operations. (Use a horizontal format.)

3. $(x^2 - 4x + 8) - (3x^2 - 6x + 1) + (4x^2 + 8x + 9)$

4. $(6t^3 + 2t^2 - t + 10) - (5t^3 + 7t + 7) - (9t^2 - t - 2)$

Reteach
Chapter 14

Name _____

What you should learn:

14.7	How to multiply a polynomial by a monomial and how to use polynomial multiplication to solve geometry problems

Correlation to Pupil's Textbook:

Chapter Test (p. 678)
Exercise 17

Examples	*Multiplying Polynomials and Using Polynomial Multiplication*

a. Find the product $-4p(p^3 - 7p^2 + 2p - 3)$.

To multiply a polynomial by a monomial, multiply each term of the polynomial by the monomial. When multiplying polynomials, you must "distribute negative signs."

$$-4p(p^3 - 7p^2 + 2p - 3) = -4p(p^3) - (-4p)(7p^2) + (-4p)(2p) - (-4p)(3) \qquad Distribute.$$

$$= -4p^4 + 28p^3 - 8p^2 + 12p \qquad Simplify.$$

b. The parallelogram at the right is divided into three regions. Write an expression for the area of each region. Then write an expression for the area of the entire region.

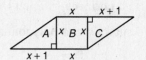

Polygon	Expression for Area	Simplify
Triangle - Region A	Area $= \frac{1}{2}x(x+1)$	$\frac{1}{2}x^2 + \frac{1}{2}x$
Square - Region B	Area $= x^2$	x^2
Triangle - Region C	Area $= \frac{1}{2}x(x+1)$	$\frac{1}{2}x^2 + \frac{1}{2}x$

To find an expression for the area of the entire region, you can add the expressions for the areas of the three regions.

Total area $= \left(\frac{1}{2}x^2 + \frac{1}{2}x\right) + (x^2) + \left(\frac{1}{2}x^2 + \frac{1}{2}x\right) = 2x^2 + x$

Guidelines:
- When multiplying polynomials, be sure to check that the signs of the product are correct.

EXERCISES

In Exercises 1–6, find the product.

1. $6n(n^2 - n)$

2. $-5(4q^3 - 7q^2 - q + 3)$

3. $4b^2(2b^2 - 5b - 1)$

4. $-z(7z^3 + 9z - 2)$

5. $-y^2(-6y^2 + 10y - 4)$

6. $2x^3(-3x^4 - 2x^3 + 8x - 6)$

In Exercises 7 and 8, use the figure at the right.

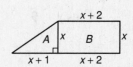

7. Write a simplified expression for the area of each region.

8. Use the result of Exercise 7 to write a simplified expression for the area of the entire region.

Reteach
Chapter 14

Name _____

What you should learn:

14.8	How to multiply a binomial by a binomial and how to use polynomial multiplication to solve real-life problems

Correlation to Pupil's Textbook:

Chapter Test (p. 678)

Exercise 18

Examples — *Multiplying Two Binomials and Solving Real-Life Problems*

a. Find the product of $(3x + 1)$ and $(x + 4)$.

Step 1: Use the Distributive Property to distribute the binomial $(3x + 1)$ over the binomial $(x + 4)$.

$$(3x + 1)(x + 4) = (3x + 1)(x) + (3x + 1)(4)$$

Step 2: Use the Distributive Property again to simplify the expressions $(3x + 1)(x) + (3x + 1)(4)$ from Step 1.

$$
\begin{aligned}
(3x + 1)(x + 4) &= (3x + 1)(x) + (3x + 1)(4) && \textit{Step 1}\\
&= (3x)(x) + (1)(x) + (3x)(4) + (1)(4) && \textit{Step 2}\\
&= 3x^2 + x + 12x + 4 && \textit{Simplify.}\\
&= 3x^2 + 13x + 4 && \textit{Simplify.}
\end{aligned}
$$

b. The area of the rectangle at the right is 72 square centimeters. Find the dimensions of the rectangle.

Verbal Model

$$\boxed{\text{Area}} = \boxed{\text{Length}} \cdot \boxed{\text{Width}}$$

Labels

Area = 72   (square centimeters)
Length = $2x + 3$ (centimeters)
Width = $x + 5$ (centimeters)

Algebraic Model

$$
\begin{aligned}
72 &= (2x + 3)(x + 5)\\
&= (2x + 3)(x) + (2x + 3)(5)\\
&= (2x)(x) + (3)(x) + (2x)(5) + (3)(5)\\
&= 2x^2 + 3x + 10x + 15\\
&= 2x^2 + 13x + 15
\end{aligned}
$$

You can use *Guess, Check, and Revise* to find the value of x for which $2x^2 + 13x + 15$ is equal to 72. Let $x = 3$: $2(3)^2 + 13(3) + 15 = 18 + 39 + 15 = 72$.

Because $x = 3$, the rectangle is 8 centimeters by 9 centimeters.

Guidelines:
- When you multiply two binomials, you use the Distributive Property twice.

EXERCISES

In Exercises 1–6, find the product using the Distributive Property.

1. $(x + 1)(7x + 5)$

2. $(2x + 4)(x + 6)$

3. $(4x + 3)(2x + 1)$

4. $(6x + 5)(5x + 6)$

5. $(3x + 2)(7x + 2)$

6. $(8x + 3)(x + 7)$

Answers to Exercises

■ Lesson 1.1 (page 1)

1. 14, 19, 24, 29, 34, 39 **2.** $\frac{1}{2}$, 1, 2, 4, 8, 16
3. 18, 15, 12, 9, 6, 3
4. Each succeeding number is 4 more than the preceding number. The next 3 terms are 23, 27, 31.
5. Each succeeding number is 10 times the preceding number. The next 3 terms are 100,000, 1,000,000, 10,000,000.
6. Each succeeding number is 5 less than the preceding number. The next 3 terms are 13, 8, 3.

■ Lesson 1.2 (page 2)

1. 339.1 **2.** 27 **3.** 918 **4.** 333
5. 91.25 **6.** 109 **7.** 0.282 **8.** 279
9. $16 + 4 = 20$ **10.** $6 = 10 - 4$

■ Lesson 1.3 (page 3)

1. The square root of 0.09 is 0.3.
2. 2 raised to the fifth power is 32.
3. The square root of 484 is 22.
4. $\left(\frac{1}{3}\right)^2$, $0.\overline{1}$ **5.** 6.7^4, 2015.1121
6. 15^3, 3375 **7.** 14.18
8. 2.14 **9.** 1.2

■ Lesson 1.4 (page 4)

1. 16 **2.** 19 **3.** 44
4. 8 **5.** 58 **6.** 26

■ Lesson 1.5 (page 5)

1. 20 **2.** 6 **3.** 4 **4.** 49 **5.** 5
6. 96 **7.** 71 **8.** 72 **9.** 360 km

■ Lesson 1.6 (page 6)

Year	1981	1982	1983	1984
Minimum	32,500	33,500	35,000	40,000
Average	185,651	241,497	289,194	329,408

Year	1985	1986	1987	1988
Minimum	60,000	60,000	62,500	62,500
Average	371,571	412,520	412,454	438,729

■ Lesson 1.6 (cont.)

Year	1989	1990	1991
Minimum	68,000	100,000	100,000
Average	497,254	597,537	851,492

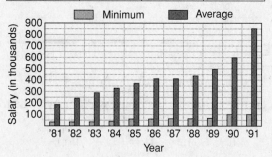

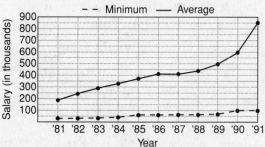

■ Lesson 1.7 (page 7)

1. Decagon **2.** Quadrilateral
3. Hexagon **4.** $\dfrac{(9)(6)}{2} = 27$

■ Lesson 1.8 (page 8)

1.

n	1	2	3	4	5
$\dfrac{240}{n}$	240	120	80	60	48

2.

n	0	1	2	3	4
$\dfrac{n^2}{3}$	0	$\dfrac{1}{3}$	$\dfrac{4}{3}$	3	$\dfrac{16}{3}$

3.

n	1	2	3	4	5
$\dfrac{n+1}{n}$	$\dfrac{2}{1}$	$\dfrac{3}{2}$	$\dfrac{4}{3}$	$\dfrac{5}{4}$	$\dfrac{6}{5}$

From the table, you can see that the numerator increases by 1 and the denominator also increases by 1.

4. $\dfrac{10(11)}{2} = 55$

■ Lesson 2.1 (page 9)

1. $3x + 6$

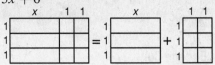

2. $2x + 2$

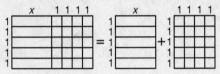

3. $8x + 12$

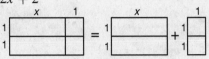

4. $5x + 20$

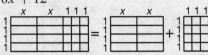

5. $88 + 56$ **6.** $10r + 60$ **7.** $x + 9$
8. $ac + 3a$ **9.** $xy + xz$ **10.** $5d + 5e + 35$
11. $14 + 7e + 35$ **12.** $pq + pr + ps$

■ Lesson 2.2 (page 10)

1. $y^2 + 5z$ **2.** $3a^2$ **3.** $5(c + d) = 5c + 5d$
4. $3(p + q) = 3p + 3q$ **5.** $13xy$ **6.** $9x + 36$

■ Lesson 2.3 (page 11)

1. No, $x = 3$ **2.** Yes **3.** No, $x = 32$
4. Yes **5.** 11 **6.** 1 **7.** 6
8. 14 **9.** 9 **10.** 3 **11.** 3 **12.** 7

■ Lesson 2.4 (page 12)

1. 42 **2.** 226 **3.** 378
4. 18.4 **5.** 23.2 **6.** 111.8

■ Lesson 2.5 (page 13)

1. 12 **2.** 14 **3.** 102 **4.** 105
5. 42.3 **6.** 16.2 **7.** 55 **8.** 7

■ Lesson 2.6 (page 14)

1.–4. Answers vary.

1. $4 + 6x$ **2.** $30 - 2n$
3. $\dfrac{k}{4 + c}$ **4.** $15 - 9y$

■ Lesson 2.7 (page 15)

1. d **2.** b **3.** a **4.** c
5.–8. Answers vary.
5. The sum of 35 and a number is 43.
6. The quotient of a number and 6 is 12.
7. 67 is the difference of a number and 7.
8. The product of 3.4 and a number is 27.2.

■ Lesson 2.8 (page 16)

1. $9000

■ Lesson 2.9 (page 17)

1. $c < 55$ **2.** $x \le 13$ **3.** $t > 30.4$
4. $y \ge 39$ **5.** $9.6 > s$ **6.** $w < 49$

■ Lesson 3.1 (page 18)

1. a number line from -2 to 7

2. a number line from -4 to 5

3. a number line from -6 to 3

4. a number line from -6 to 4

5. $5, 5$ **6.** $-14, 14$ **7.** $15, 15$ **8.** $-33, 33$

■ Lesson 3.2 (page 19)

1. $-9 + 12 = 3$ **2.** $5 + (-14) = -9$
3. $7 + 11 = 18$ **4.** $0 + (-17) = -17$
5. $-23 + 4 = -19$ **6.** $-11 + (-13) = -24$
7. $6 + 0 = 6$ **8.** $8 + (-8) = 0$

■ Lesson 3.3 (page 20)

1. $-8 + 3 + 7 = 2$ **2.** $5 + (-3) + (-9) = -7$
3. $13 + 4 + (-5) = 12$ **4.** $5x + 7, 22$
5. $-5x + 3, -12$ **6.** $x, 3$

■ Lesson 3.4 (page 21)

1. $11 - 16 = -5$ **2.** $24 - (-3) = 27$
3. $-18 - 9 = -27$ **4.** $-15 - (-4) = -11$
5. $0 - 33 = -33$ **6.** $35 - 6 = 29$
7. $0 - (-13) = 13$ **8.** $-5 - 5 = -10$
9. $3n + (-5n) + m; 3n, -5n, m$
10. $8x + (-3x) + (-4); 8x, -3x, -4$

■ Lesson 3.4 (page 21 cont.)

11. $7a + (-9b) + (-6); 7a, -9b, -6$

12. $-11x + 8, -14$

13. $-19x + 10, -28$ **14.** $4x, 8$

■ Lesson 3.5 (page 22)

1. $4(-5) = -20$ **2.** $(-9)(-8) = 72$

3. $-10 \cdot 2 = -20$ **4.** $15(1) = 15$

5. 6 **6.** -12 **7.** -18 **8.** -4

■ Lesson 3.6 (page 23)

1. 22 **2.** -15 **3.** -16 **4.** 5 **5.** 0

6. 11 **7.** 15 **8.** -26 **9.** -2 **10.** -11

■ Lesson 3.7 (page 24)

1. $-11, -11 + 7 = -4$ **2.** $11, 11 - 17 = -6$

3. $-6, 54 = (-9)(-6)$

4. $-45, -45/15 = -3$

5. $-30, -35 = -30 - 5$

6. $-\frac{1}{2}, 6 = -12\left(-\frac{1}{2}\right)$

7. $20, -10 = \dfrac{20}{-2}$ **8.** $-3, 19 = -3 + 22$

■ Lesson 3.8 (page 25)

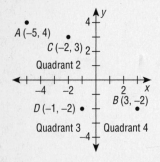

■ Lesson 4.1 (page 26)

1. 3 **2.** -4 **3.** 30 **4.** 3

5. 4 **6.** 56

■ Lesson 4.2 (page 27)

1. 1 **2.** 1 **3.** 9 **4.** 4

5. -9 **6.** -2 **7.** 640

■ Lesson 4.3 (page 28)

1. $\frac{1}{13}$ **2.** -6 **3.** $-\frac{1}{4}$ **4.** 2 **5.** 27

6. -2 **7.** 32 **8.** 5 feet by 9 feet

■ Lesson 4.4 (page 29)

1. 2 **2.** 26 **3.** -8 **4.** -1

5. -27 **6.** 2

■ Lesson 4.5 (page 30)

1. 12 **2.** 5 **3.** -3 **4.** 2

5. -15 **6.** 2 **7.** 6

■ Lesson 4.6 (page 31)

1.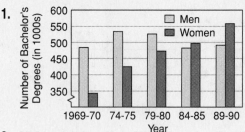

2. 275

■ Lesson 4.7 (page 32)

1. 0.98 **2.** 3.28 **3.** 1.12

4. -64.46 **5.** -3.59 **6.** 11 ounces

■ Lesson 4.8 (page 33)

1. 2, 2 units by 10 units

2. 5, 6 units by 21 units

3. 8, 8 units by 8 units

4. 1420 miles

■ Lesson 5.1 (page 34)

1. Transamerica Pyramid and John Hancock Tower

2.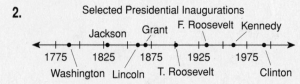

■ Lesson 5.2 (page 35)

1.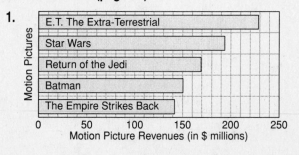

2. The totals will change to 5, 2, 2, 2, and 3.

Lesson 5.3 (page 36)

1. 17,000; 53,000   **2.** 17,000; 60,000

3. 1970-1975   **4.** 1985-1990

Lesson 5.4 (page 37)

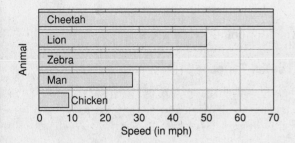

Lesson 5.5 (page 38)

It appears that natural gas heating decreased significantly from 1980 to 1985. The broken vertical scale accentuates the change, which actually is a very small decrease.

Lesson 5.6 (page 39)

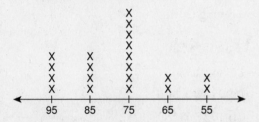

It appears that sixteen of the twenty students passed the biology exam.

Lesson 5.7 (page 40)

1. Positive correlation

2. Negative correlation

3. No correlation

4. Positive correlation

Lesson 5.8 (page 41)

1. $\frac{1}{4}$ or 0.25   **2.** $\frac{3}{4}$ or 0.75

3. $\frac{1}{2}$ or 0.50   **4.** $\frac{1}{2}$ or 0.50

Lesson 6.1 (page 42)

1. Yes: 3, 5; No: 2, 4, 6, 8, 9, 10

2. Yes: 2, 3, 6; No: 4, 5, 8, 9, 10

3. Yes: 5; No: 2, 3, 4, 6, 8, 9, 10

4. Yes: 2, 4, 5, 10; No: 3, 6, 8, 9

5. Yes: 2, 3, 4, 5, 6, 8, 9, 10

6. Yes: 2, 3, 6, 9; No: 4, 5, 8, 10

7. Yes: 2, 3, 4, 5, 6, 8, 9, 10

8. Yes: 2, 4, 8; No: 3, 5, 6, 9, 10

9. 1, 3, 5, 15

10. 1, 2, 3, 4, 6, 8, 12, 16, 24, 48

11. 1, 3, 5, 15, 25, 75

12. 1, 2, 47, 94

13. 1, 2, 4, 8, 11, 22, 44, 88

14. 1, 2, 3, 6, 9, 18, 27, 54

15. 1, 2, 5, 7, 10, 14, 35, 70

16. 1, 3, 7, 9, 21, 63

Lesson 6.2 (page 43)

1. $5 \cdot 7$ **2.** $2 \cdot 7^2$ **3.** $2 \cdot 3 \cdot 13$

4. $2^2 \cdot 3 \cdot 5$ **5.** $2 \cdot 3 \cdot 7$

6. $2^3 \cdot 7$ **7.** $2 \cdot 3^3$ **8.** $2^3 \cdot 11$

9. $(-1) \cdot 2 \cdot 2 \cdot 2 \cdot 2 \cdot p \cdot p \cdot q, (-1) \cdot 2^4 \cdot p^2 \cdot q$

10. $(-1) \cdot 2 \cdot 3 \cdot 3 \cdot a \cdot a \cdot a \cdot b \cdot b \cdot b \cdot b$,
$(-1) \cdot 2 \cdot 3^2 \cdot a^3 \cdot b^4$

11. $2 \cdot 2 \cdot 5 \cdot c \cdot d \cdot d, 2^2 \cdot 5 \cdot c \cdot d^2$

12. $2 \cdot 5 \cdot 7 \cdot x \cdot x \cdot y \cdot y \cdot y \cdot y$,
$2 \cdot 5 \cdot 7 \cdot x^2 \cdot y^4$

13. Composite   **14.** Prime

15. Prime   **16.** Composite

Lesson 6.3 (page 44)

1. $6x$ **2.** 42   **3.** 101   **4.** $25ab$

5. 98   **6.** 5   **7.** 45   **8.** $4p^2$

Lesson 6.4 (page 45)

1. $20 = 2 \cdot 2 \cdot 5, 25 = 5 \cdot 5$,
LCM $= 2 \cdot 2 \cdot 5 \cdot 5 = 100$

2. $7x = 7 \cdot x, 10x^3 = 2 \cdot 5 \cdot x \cdot x \cdot x$,
LCM $= 2 \cdot 5 \cdot 7 \cdot x \cdot x \cdot x = 70x^3$

3. $145 = 5 \cdot 29, 155 = 5 \cdot 31$,
LCM $= 5 \cdot 29 \cdot 31 = 4495$

4. $18 = 2 \cdot 3 \cdot 3, 22 = 2 \cdot 11$,
LCM $= 2 \cdot 3 \cdot 3 \cdot 11 = 198$

5. $4a^2b = 2 \cdot 2 \cdot a \cdot a \cdot b, 5ab^2 = 5 \cdot a \cdot b \cdot b$,
LCM $= 2 \cdot 2 \cdot 5 \cdot a \cdot a \cdot b \cdot b = 20a^2b^2$

6. $13p^2 = 13 \cdot p \cdot p, 26p^3 = 2 \cdot 13 \cdot p \cdot p \cdot p$,
LCM $= 2 \cdot 13 \cdot p \cdot p \cdot p = 26p^3$

7. $120 = 2 \cdot 2 \cdot 2 \cdot 3 \cdot 5$, $200 = 2 \cdot 2 \cdot 2 \cdot 5 \cdot 5$,
LCM $= 2 \cdot 2 \cdot 2 \cdot 3 \cdot 5 \cdot 5 = 600$

8. $196 = 2 \cdot 2 \cdot 7 \cdot 7$, $220 = 2 \cdot 2 \cdot 5 \cdot 11$,
LCM $= 2 \cdot 2 \cdot 5 \cdot 7 \cdot 7 \cdot 11 = 10{,}780$

■ Lesson 6.5 (page 46)

1. $6, \frac{2}{7}$ **2.** $8, \frac{4}{7}$ **3.** $15, \frac{3}{4}$ **4.** $14, \frac{3}{7}$
5. $<$ **6.** $>$ **7.** $<$ **8.** $=$

■ Lesson 6.6 (page 47)

1. $0.8\overline{3}$, repeating, rational

2. 0.68, terminating, rational

3. $2.236068\ldots$, non-repeating, irrational

4. 2.875, terminating, rational

5. $\frac{23}{50}$ **6.** $\frac{7}{5}$ **7.** $\frac{43}{25}$ **8.** $\frac{23}{10}$
9. $\frac{66}{25}$ **10.** $\frac{9}{20}$ **11.** $\frac{3}{40}$ **12.** $\frac{3}{20}$

■ Lesson 6.7 (page 48)

1. $\frac{1}{12}$ **2.** 1 **3.** $-\frac{1}{49}$ **4.** x^7
5. 8^4 or 4096 **6.** $\frac{1}{t^3}$
7. 2^5 or 32 **8.** d^5

■ Lesson 6.8 (page 49)

1. 4.989×10^4 **2.** 1.2×10^{-1}
3. 5.66×10^7 **4.** 8.9×10^{-5}
5. 567 **6.** 0.0000032 **7.** 0.229
8. $1{,}380{,}000{,}000$
9. 1.005×10^{-1}; 0.1005 grams per cubic centimeter.

■ Lesson 6.9 (page 50)

1. 1; deficient

2. $1, 2, 3, 6, 9$; abundant

3. 1; deficient

4. $1, 2, 4, 5, 10$; abundant

5. $n(n-1)$; $20, 30, 42$

6. $n^2 + 2$; $27, 38, 51$

7.

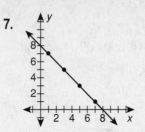

The four points lie on a line.

■ Lesson 7.1 (page 51)

1. $\frac{6}{7}$ **2.** $-\frac{9}{13}$ **3.** $\frac{9}{5}$ **4.** $\frac{2}{5}$
5. $\frac{5x}{3}$ **6.** $\frac{-a}{3}$ **7.** $\frac{3}{4y}$ **8.** $\frac{-b}{3}$
9. $x = \frac{8}{3}$ **10.** $n = \frac{1}{6}$
11. $s = -\frac{16}{9}$ **12.** $z = \frac{1}{4}$

■ Lesson 7.2 (page 52)

1. $-\frac{1}{10}$ **2.** $\frac{35}{36}$ **3.** $-\frac{7}{6}$ **4.** $-\frac{5}{8}$
5. $\frac{5a}{14}$ **6.** $\frac{x}{14}$ **7.** $\frac{4q + 5p}{pq}$ **8.** $\frac{y - 22}{2y}$
9. $\frac{1}{2}$ of a percentage point

■ Lesson 7.3 (page 53)

1. $0.563 + 0.286$; 0.85

2. $0.182 - 0.895$; -0.71

3. $0.133x + 0.172x$; $0.31x$

4. $1 - (0.222 + 0.273)$; 0.51

5. $2.1 + 4.125 - 1.75$; 4.48

6. $0.308n - 0.051n + 0.176n$; $0.43n$

■ Lesson 7.4 (page 54)

1. $\frac{12}{35}$ **2.** $-\frac{4}{11}$ **3.** $\frac{221}{24}$ **4.** $\frac{169}{27}$
5. $-\frac{15x}{13}$ **6.** $\frac{15}{7}$ **7.** $\frac{17}{10t}$ **8.** $\frac{1}{9}$

■ Lesson 7.5 (page 55)

1. $-\frac{2}{7}$ **2.** $-\frac{1}{2}$ **3.** 11 **4.** $\frac{3}{4}$
5. $\frac{x}{5}$ **6.** $-\frac{4y}{9}$ **7.** $98z$ **8.** $\frac{4}{5}$

■ Lesson 7.6 (page 56)

1. 20% **2.** 35% **3.** 32% **4.** 80%
5. 50% **6.** 25% **7.** 10% **8.** 75%

Lesson 7.7 (page 57)

1. 0.58   **2.** 1.2   **3.** 0.023   **4.** 0.634
5. 40%   **6.** 3.3%   **7.** 324%   **8.** 0.2%
9. 12.5%   **10.** 60%   **11.** 375%   **12.** 175%

Lesson 7.8 (page 58)

1. 0.15, 18   **2.** 0.07, 35   **3.** 1.25, 20
4. 2.40, 192   **5.** d; 22.5   **6.** b; 90
7. a; 135   **8.** c; 120   **9.** $6.00

Lesson 7.9 (page 59)

1. $78,480
2. Possible conclusions: Nearly all homes with TV's have color TV's. Over half of the homes with TV's have cable.

Lesson 8.1 (page 60)

1. Ratio, 8/15
2. Rate, 11/2 yards per carry
3. Rate, 75 revolutions per minute
4. 220 meters/4000 meters, 11/200
5. 9 feet/12 feet, 3/4
6. 3520 yards/2640 yards, 4/3
7. $\approx$ 1.79 inches per hour
8. $4.50 per hour

Lesson 8.2 (page 61)

1. 12   **2.** 40   **3.** $\frac{7}{6}$
4. $\frac{3}{4} = \frac{9}{x}$, 12   **5.** $\frac{x}{10} = \frac{5}{4}$, $\frac{25}{2}$
6. $\frac{1}{8} = \frac{y}{4}$, $\frac{1}{2}$ **7.** 10

Lesson 8.3 (page 62)

1. 35 inches

Lesson 8.4 (page 63)

1. 50.4   **2.** 24   **3.** 44%
4. 383.33%   **5.** 390.53   **6.** 28

Lesson 8.5 (page 64)

1. "less than 15 hours"- 5 students, "15-20 hours"- 10 students
2. $9.90, 22%

Lesson 8.6 (page 65)

1. Increase, about 35.4%
2. Decrease, about 4.5%

Lesson 8.7 (page 66)

1. $5 \cdot 6 = 30$
2. 10 different kinds

Lesson 8.8 (page 67)

1. $\frac{3}{12} = \frac{1}{4}$ **2.** $\frac{2}{12} = \frac{1}{6}$ **3.** $\frac{1}{12}$
4. $\frac{1}{12}$ **5.** $\frac{5}{12}$ **6.** $\frac{3}{12} = \frac{1}{4}$

Lesson 9.1 (page 68)

1. $\sqrt{26}, -\sqrt{26}$ **2.** 14, -14 **3.** $\sqrt{47}, -\sqrt{47}$
4. 18, -18 **5.** $\frac{3}{7}, -\frac{3}{7}$ **6.** 0.8, -0.8
7. $\frac{4}{9}, -\frac{4}{9}$ **8.** 30, -30 **9.** 2, -2
10. 4.583, -4.583 **11.** 3, -3
12. 1.333, -1.333 **13.** 6 ft $\times$ 6 ft

Lesson 9.2 (page 69)

1. 3.605551275 ..., nonrepeating, irrational
2. 0.6, terminating, rational
3. $0.\overline{09}$, repeating, rational
4. -2.5, terminating, rational
5. a   **6.** d   **7.** b   **8.** c

Lesson 9.3 (page 70)

1. About 9.8   **2.** 15   **3.** About 31.6
4. About 7.6   **5.** 5   **6.** 80

Lesson 9.4 (page 71)

1. 51 feet

Lesson 9.5 (page 72)

1. ![number line with open circle at 4]
2. ![number line with closed dot at -2]
3. ![number line with open circle at 0]
4. ![number line with closed dot at -3]
5. $n \leq 1$

![number line with closed dot at 1]

6. $x > -1$

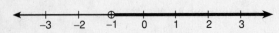

7. $z \geq -4$

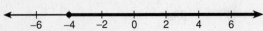

8. $-8 > a$ **9.** $0 \leq t$ **10.** $7 \geq w$

■ **Lesson 9.6 (page 73)**

1. $y \geq -3$

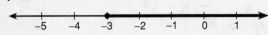

2. $x < -3$

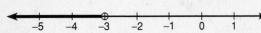

3. $-10 > a$

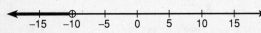

4. $n \geq -5$

5. $-8 \leq s$

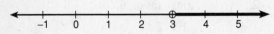

6. $x > 3$

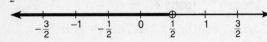

7. $\frac{1}{2} > b$

8. $t \geq -6$

■ **Lesson 9.7 (page 74)**

1. $x \geq 3$ **2.** $a > 8$ **3.** $y > 1$
4. $n \geq -5$ **5.** $x \geq 1$ **6.** $x < 3$
7. 6 hours

■ **Lesson 9.8 (page 75)**

1. t   **2.** q   **3.** s   **4.** t
5. $x > 5$ and $x < 23$
6. $x > 8$ and $x < 28$
7. $x > 4$ and $x < 18$

■ **Lesson 10.1 (page 76)**

1. $\overleftrightarrow{AC}, \overleftrightarrow{AE}$ **2.** $\overrightarrow{EA}, \overrightarrow{EB}, \overrightarrow{EC}, \overrightarrow{ED}$
3. E   **4.** $\overline{DE}, \overline{EB}, \overline{DB}$

■ **Lesson 10.2 (page 77)**

1. d   **2.** c   **3.** a   **4.** b
5. $\angle EIH, \angle EFG$ **6.** $\angle EIF, \angle FIH, \angle IHG$
7. $\angle IEF, \angle EFI, \angle FGH$ **8.** $\angle IFG$

■ **Lesson 10.3 (page 78)**

1. $\angle 1$ and $\angle 4$, $\angle 2$ and $\angle 3$, $\angle 5$ and $\angle 8$, $\angle 6$ and $\angle 7$
2. $\angle 1$ and $\angle 5$, $\angle 3$ and $\angle 7$, $\angle 2$ and $\angle 6$, $\angle 4$ and $\angle 8$
3. $\angle 1, \angle 4, \angle 5, \angle 8$ **4.** $\angle 2, \angle 3, \angle 6, \angle 7$

■ **Lesson 10.4 (page 79)**

1. Vertical line symmetry
2. Rotational symmetry (120° in both directions), 3 lines of symmetry
3. Rotational symmetry (72° and 144° in both directions), 5 lines of symmetry
4. Horizontal line symmetry

■ **Lesson 10.5 (page 80)**

1. Isosceles, acute   **2.** Scalene, right
3. Equilateral, equiangular
4. Scalene, obtuse

■ **Lesson 10.6 (page 81)**

1. Rectangle   **2.** Square
3. Parallelogram   **4.** Always
5. Never   **6.** Sometimes   **7.** Always

■ **Lesson 10.7 (page 82)**

1. Pentagon, yes
2. Rhombus, no   **3.** Hexagon, no

■ **Lesson 10.8 (page 83)**

1. $m\angle 4 = 140°$, $m\angle 6 = 70°$

■ **Lesson 10.9 (page 84)**

1. $\angle R, \angle Q, \overline{PQ}, \overline{PR}$
2. $\angle Z, \angle Y, \overline{XY}, \overline{XZ}$
3. $\angle E, \angle C, \overline{CD}, \overline{DE}$
4. 75°   **5.** 75°   **6.** 30°

■ **Lesson 11.1 (page 85)**

1. $A = 30$ sq units, $P \approx 2\sqrt{40} + 10$ units ≈ 22.6 units

2. $A = 32$ sq units, $P \approx 26$ units

3. $A = \frac{35}{2}$ sq units, $P = \sqrt{74} + 12 \approx 20.6$ units

4. $A_1 = 75$ sq units, $A_2 = 2(75) = 150$ sq units or $A_2 = 10(15) = 150$ sq units

■ **Lesson 11.2 (page 86)**

1. $\angle L$ 2. $\overline{JL}$ 3. $\angle C$

4. $\overline{CD}$ 5. $\overline{KL}$ 6. $\angle K$

■ **Lesson 11.3 (page 87)**

1. $\triangle DEF$ 2. $\triangle GHI$

3. $\triangle ABC$ 4. $\triangle ABC$

■ **Lesson 11.4 (page 88)**

1. $60°$ clockwise

2. $120°$ counterclockwise

3. $90°$ counterclockwise

■ **Lesson 11.5 (page 89)**

1. b   2. a   3. c

■ **Lesson 11.6 (page 90)**

1. $m\angle J = m\angle W, m\angle K = m\angle X, m\angle L = m\angle Y, m\angle M = m\angle Z$

2. $\dfrac{JK}{WX} = \dfrac{KL}{XY} = \dfrac{LM}{YZ} = \dfrac{MJ}{ZW}$

3. $\frac{3}{5}$ 4. $XY = 1.8, JM = 8$

■ **Lesson 11.7 (page 91)**

1. $\dfrac{\text{Area of actual painting}}{\text{Area of sketch}} = \dfrac{1728 \text{ sq inches}}{48 \text{ sq inches}} = \dfrac{36}{1}$

■ **Lesson 11.8 (page 92)**

1. $2/\sqrt{29} \approx 0.37$ 2. $5/\sqrt{29} \approx 0.93$

3. $2/\sqrt{29} \approx 0.37$ 4. $\frac{5}{2}$

5. $5/\sqrt{29} \approx 0.93$ 6. $\frac{2}{5}$

7. $\sqrt{3}/2 \approx 0.87, 1/2, \sqrt{3} \approx 1.73$

■ **Lesson 11.9 (page 93)**

1. 10.46   2. 9.77   3. 21.25

4. 12.72   5. ≈ 5.07 feet

■ **Lesson 12.1 (page 94)**

1. $C = 5.7$ cm; $A = 2.5$ sq cm

2. $C = 100.5$ cm; $A = 803.8$ sq cm

3. $C = 28.3$ in.; $A = 63.6$ sq in.

4. $C = 7.9$ in.; $A = 4.9$ sq in.

■ **Lesson 12.2 (page 95)**

1. a. edge; b. face; c. vertex

2. a. base; b. lateral surface

3. a. vertex; b. edge; c. face

4. a. base; b. lateral surface

5. Prism

■ **Lesson 12.3 (page 96)**

1. 96 sq in.   2. 130π sq cm ≈ 408.2 sq cm

■ **Lesson 12.4 (page 97)**

1. 120 in.^{3} 2. 35 cm^3

3. 540 cm^3 4. 70.2 ft^3

■ **Lesson 12.5 (page 98)**

1. 84.78 in.^{3} 2. 50.24 ft^3

3. 78.5 cm^3 4. 10.99 in.^{3}

5. The unit price of a quart is 0.0303 and the unit price of a liter is 0.0322. The quart is the better buy.

■ **Lesson 12.6 (page 99)**

1. 35 cm^3 2. $\frac{64}{3}$ or $21.\overline{3}$ m^3

3. About 314 in.^{3} 4. About 932.58 ft^3

■ **Lesson 12.7 (page 100)**

1. 195.33 in.^{3} 2. 2143.57 in.^{3}

3. 11,488.21 cm^3 4. 143.72 in.^{3}

5. ≈ 8 cm

■ **Lesson 12.8 (page 101)**

1. $\frac{2}{1}$ 2. 160π sq units ≈ 502.4 sq units

3. 40π sq units ≈ 125.6 sq units

■ Lesson 13.1 (page 102)

1. Possible solutions:

x	0	5	10	20
y	4	3	2	0

2. Possible solutions:

x	−2	−1	0	1	2
y	−10	−8	−6	−4	−2

3. Possible solutions:

x	−2	0	2	4	6
y	−12	−9	−6	−3	0

4. 121 pounds   **5.** 5.5 kg

■ Lesson 13.2 (page 103)

1. No; Possible solution: $(−1, 10)$

2. No; Possible solution: $(2, 5)$

3. Yes

4. 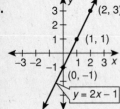   **5.**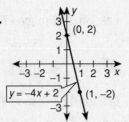

6.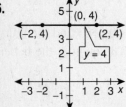

■ Lesson 13.3 (page 103)

1. x-intercept: 7; y-intercept: 7

2. x-intercept: 3; y-intercept: −6

3. x-intercept: −6; y-intercept: 3

4. x-intercept: 6; y-intercept: −8

5. 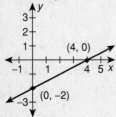   **6.**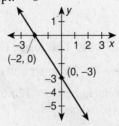

7.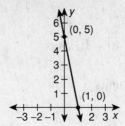

■ Lesson 13.4 (page 105)

1. $\frac{1}{4}$ **2.** $−1$ **3.** 0

4. $m = −\frac{3}{2}$ **5.** $m = 2$

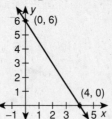 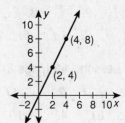

6. $m = 0$

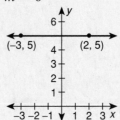

■ Lesson 13.5 (page 106)

1. b   **2.** a   **3.** c

4. $m = −\frac{4}{3}; b = −2$ **5.** $m = \frac{1}{2}; b = 0$

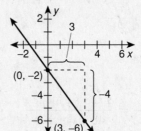 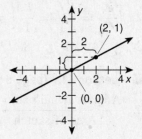

6. $m = \frac{1}{2}; b = −\frac{3}{2}$

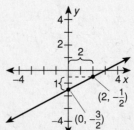

■ Lesson 13.6 (page 107)

1. $10 · $\boxed{\begin{array}{c}\text{Number of}\\ \text{T-shirts}\end{array}}$ + $15 $\boxed{\begin{array}{c}\text{Number of}\\ \text{Sweatshirts}\end{array}}$

   = $1500

   $10x + 15y = 1500$

2.

x	0	30	60	90	120	150
y	100	80	60	40	20	0

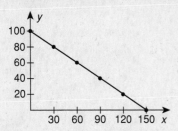

3. When no T-shirts are sold, 100 sweatshirts must be sold in order to raise $1500. When no sweatshirts are sold, 150 T-shirts must be sold in order to raise $1500.

4. About 4.2 million cruise passengers

■ Lesson 13.7 (page 108)

1. c; yes; no   2. d; no; yes

3. a; no; yes   4. b; no; yes

■ Lesson 13.8 (page 109)

1. Estimates vary; 5

2. Estimates vary; $\sqrt{29} \approx 5.39$

3. Estimates vary; (0,0)

4. Estimates vary; (1, 0)

■ Lesson 14.1 (page 110)

1. 45.2; 44.5; 42   2. 14.3; 15; 12

■ Lesson 14.2 (page 111)

1.

Unordered plot

3	396570
2	490328286856
1	37180592

2 | 4 represents 24

Ordered Plot

3	035679
2	022345668889
1	01235789

2 | 0 represents 20

10, 11, 12, 13, 15, 17, 18, 19, 20, 22, 22, 23, 24, 25, 26, 26, 28, 28, 28, 29, 30, 33, 35, 36, 37, 39

2. Ordered data on the left: 2, 3, 21, 25, 25, 27, 31, 32; Ordered data on the right: 2, 5, 8, 27, 29, 34, 36

■ Lesson 14.3 (page 112)

1. 24, 44, 32, 37, 42; Possible answer: The youngest teacher is 24 years old and the oldest teacher is 44 years old. The median age for these teachers is 37.

2.

```
      ┌─────┬─────────┐
●─────┤     │         ├────────────●
3     └─────┴─────────┘            19
      8    11        15
```

■ Lesson 14.4 (page 112)

1. $\begin{bmatrix} 7 & 2 \\ 4 & -5 \end{bmatrix}, \begin{bmatrix} 7 & -4 \\ 20 & 13 \end{bmatrix}$

2. $\begin{bmatrix} -2 & -7 & -2 \\ 17 & 1 & -9 \end{bmatrix}, \begin{bmatrix} -8 & -7 & 10 \\ 3 & 3 & -19 \end{bmatrix}$

3.

	Sale price	Regular price
Shirts	13.00	18.50
Jeans	21.00	29.00
Belts	8.50	12.00

■ Lesson 14.5 (page 114)

1. $5x^2 + 4x + 3$; trinomial

2. $4w^2 + 15$; binomial

3. $5y^2 - 4y$; binomial

■ Lesson 14.6 (page 115)

1. $7y^3 - 2y^2 - 4$ 2. $8m^4 - 5m^3 - 5m + 9$

3. $2x^2 + 10x + 16$ 4. $t^3 - 7t^2 - 7t + 5$

■ Lesson 14.7 (page 116)

1. $6n^3 - 6n^2$ 2. $-20q^3 + 35q^2 + 5q - 15$

3. $8b^4 - 20b^3 - 4b^2$ 4. $-7z^4 - 9z^2 + 2z$

5. $6y^4 - 10y^3 + 4y^2$

6. $-6x^7 - 4x^6 + 16x^4 - 12x^3$

7. Region A: $\frac{1}{2}x^2 + \frac{1}{2}x$

   Region B: $x^2 + 2x$

8. $\frac{3}{2}x^2 + \frac{5}{2}x$

■ Lesson 14.8 (page 117)

1. $7x^2 + 12x + 5$ 2. $2x^2 + 16x + 24$

3. $8x^2 + 10x + 3$ 4. $30x^2 + 61x + 30$

5. $21x^2 + 20x + 4$ 6. $8x^2 + 59x + 21$